CW00418767

I have known Bamidele for m
time span, I have known her t
est, have a great love for Goc
character. These fine qualities a
fering of this book. *Navigating*
with such vulnerability that reassures readers and offers them
relatability and the strength to go through, knowing that it
is possible to experience such trauma and still positively live
life in its new form.

I strongly believe this book will be a great resource for
individuals going through trauma of any kind, those with the
responsibility of caring for them as well as corporate organisations with affected employees.

Rev Lara Akinola
Liberty Evangelical Ministries International

This is the remarkable memoir of my dearest friend Bamidele.
It is a revelation. In it, she shows how she has been trans-
formed over the four decades of her existence from a young
girl to a lady with a marvellous mind. I was a cancer patient
caregiver to my mother, who lost the battle five years ago,
and the book brings back poignant memories of the ripple
effects of serious illness. This is the story of a strong and beautiful woman who—despite the several challenges of abuse,
domestic violence, cultural stigma, and serious illness—has
persevered and overcome. This book is an intriguing read,
not just because it is brilliantly written but because it offers
the reader hope in the form of applicable tools to turn their
lives around after adversity. I will recommend *Navigating Your
New Normal* to anyone who has ever gone through trauma
and desires to find life fulfilment in its aftermath.

Mary Ojulari
CFO Forbes Africa

Fantastic book. I have known Bamidele for over a decade and had the privilege of walking with her through some of the seasons described in this book. This book will be of great help to those who have gone through any kind of traumatic experience as well as those who are caring for, dealing with, or helping anyone who has gone through a traumatic experience. Quite frankly, this book is for everyone, as we will all be in one of those shoes at one point or the other, and we will need help navigating our new normal.

Jaunty Aidamenbor
Compliance Manager
Seadrill Canada Ltd

Having conducted research and worked with women who have undergone complex breast reconstruction, I have observed that the impact of these traumatic circumstances on their lives cannot be overestimated.

Having gone through the same process herself, Bamidele has come through on the other side of the trauma offering credibility and authenticity.

Navigating Your New Normal offers practical steps for anyone who desires life fulfilment instead of mere survival after going through serious illness, as well as other forms of trauma. By acknowledging the impact on loved ones in the aftermath of trauma, this book also offers them tools to thrive in their own new normal journey.

I will recommend this book to those affected by trauma as well as their loved ones as it encourages them to live and celebrate full lives in the aftermath.

Dr Sarah Wright
Programme Manager for Wales and Lead
for Education at Patients Know Best

NAVIGATING YOUR NEW NORMAL

A Roadmap for Life Fulfilment After Trauma

Dear Deanne
YOU ARE A VICTOR!

B Adenipekun

Bamidele Adenipekun

Published by Author Academy Elite
PO Box 43
Powell, OH, 43035

www.AuthorAcademyElite.com

Paperback: 978-1-64085-070-5
Hardback: 978-1-64085-071-2
Ebook: 978-1-64085-072-9

Library of Congress Control Number: 2017909499

*Dedicated to the memory of my beloved sister Titi
who exemplified courage and grace in her
new normal journey till the very end.*

*Your unwavering belief in me spurs me
on to greater achievements.*

Contents

NEW NORMAL

Foreword

Adversity of one kind or another is an inescapable part of life. It comes in different forms and varying degrees. Indeed, the only ones who are free from life's adverse events are the ones who are dead. To acknowledge this truth is to position oneself for timely healing and restoration.

I believe that *Navigating Your New Normal* helps with this because it is written in such a way that it walks the reader through Bamidele's life journey, offering practical help and support throughout. The brilliance of this book is that the principles in it can apply to all types of trauma. The lives of all those affected, as well as their loved ones, are permanently altered, most often in negative ways. This is particularly true with respect to serious illness, injury, or bereavement.

As one who has both cared for family members diagnosed with cancer as well as personally being diagnosed with the same illness, Bamidele has done a great job in capturing the ramifications of the effects of such adverse circumstance on both the sufferer and their loved ones. The empathetic understanding that comes from lived experience is of immense value to the readers who will find hope and encouragement from the book.

The seven-step framework is designed to give readers practical steps towards life fulfilment in the aftermath of trauma. Even though the new normal journey is often drastically different to the life enjoyed before, it should not be any less satisfying, and that is the theme that runs all the way through the book.

Perhaps the most poignant part of this book is Bamidele's application of the framework to herself in the midst of personal tragedy. That lends added authenticity to the efficacy of the seven steps.

If you want to transition from survival to thriving in your own new normal journey, this book is for you.

Kary Oberbrunner—Author of *ELIXIR Project,*
Day Job to Dream Job, The Deeper Path,
and *Your Secret Name*

Introduction

'Weeping may endure for a night, but joy comes in the morning.'

– Psalm 30:5 (NKJV)

Difficult seasons are realities of life. None of us can escape them, regardless of geographical location, socioeconomic status, or background. For many people, these difficulties come in the shape of serious illness, injury, or bereavement. These traumatic events often change the lives of those affected beyond all recognition. They are never the same again.

When disaster or loss hits (such as serious illness or the death of close relatives), how do you respond? How do you know what to do? We will all have our share of trauma, and it is safe to say that we must figure out how to cope. Every situation requires an appropriate response. Sometimes, the wrong reaction may be as harmful as the trauma itself – leading to a 'double whammy' of suffering.

That is why I wrote this book.

You are probably reading this to find help for yourself or ideas for supporting someone else who is going through a traumatic experience. Nothing prepares you adequately for handling these situations, and that is where other people's stories come in.

The story that I am about to write is one I never thought I would tell anyone besides close friends and family. It is a story of the Father's amazing grace, His fathomless love, mercy, and the sheer wonder of His power at work in my life.

Even though I am weak and broken, God does not despise my weaknesses. Rather, He steps into them with me and enfolds me in His loving embrace – that is, if I let Him. He knows my sorrows, and He cares. What an extravagant love!

Parts of this story are uncomfortable, heart-rending, painful, fanciful, and humorous. It is the story of every human being who has ever been through trying times. Many other books can give you the scientific facts on loss and illness. I do not have the knowledge or expertise to add to that body of work. My account is from the perspective of a teenage caregiver, sister, and patient. I know the impact that a diagnosis of serious illness can have on patients and their loved ones.

This is an invitation to my life, to see how I am being enabled to put my hope and trust in the Lord despite the odds. It is a recognition that the trajectory of dealing with illness does not have to be the same for everyone. Our prayers are not always answered in the ways we want, but the same amazing grace is available and more than sufficient to help us handle life's disappointments.

My story is a celebration of life – not the one that I initially planned, but a fulfilling one of hope and joy beyond trauma.

Part I

Broken Pieces

1

The Prison
I Called Home

*'What I fear most is power with impunity. I fear
the abuse of power and the power to abuse.'*

— *Isabel Allende*

Never in a million years did I think I would tell my story
in a book. However, there comes a time when you realise
that the message you have is in your mess, and the gospel
you must preach is in what you have gone through. My
life has been a series of navigating various 'new normals'
and finding that grace abides on the other side of every
storm – that is, if one survives the storm. My story tells of
how to survive whatever storms come one's way and what
to do when you must navigate a new normal.

My name is Bamidele Adenipekun. I was born in London to Nigerian parents who had come to the UK to study.
Prior to coming to the UK, my older sister Titi was born
in Nigeria. She spent some years living with my mum's
parents. She later joined the family here in the UK. I was
the first of three children born to my parents in the UK.
When I was two years old, I was taken to Nigeria by my

paternal uncle and his wife. Four years later, my parents moved back to Nigeria with my younger brother and sister, leaving Titi behind in the UK where she eventually became a ward of the state. After the move to Nigeria, my parents had another child, so I grew up with four siblings. My older sister was not reintegrated into the family until a year after my mum's death.

Although I was born in the UK, I spent my formative years in Nigeria. I was raised by a father whose brand of discipline was rigid and physically violent. His philosophy was that he could justify any wicked act or punishment and no-one could question him because he was of superior intelligence. If he had to instil fear in his children to achieve his aims, then the end justified the means.

In Nigeria, child abuse is not recognised as a crime; children need discipline, and however the parents mete it out is deemed acceptable. The child is blamed for incurring the wrath of the parents just like women are often blamed for pushing men to beat them black and blue.

It is fair to say that every society has its own brand of dysfunction which, despite good intentions, cannot be fixed. Where there is law and order, the oppressed and abused still fall through the cracks. But in a society where certain laws and the prospect of real justice is absent, it is unfortunate that wicked acts will continue with impunity.

While there is now increasing awareness in Nigeria that domestic violence within adult relationships is unacceptable, the whole concept of child abuse (be it physical, sexual, verbal, emotional, etc.), overall, is still a silent issue. Child victims are voiceless in a culture that opines that elders know best and out of respect they should never be challenged.

Even by Nigerian standards, my father was a terror. He ruled with an iron fist. He would often beat us at the least provocation. The beating was grossly disproportionate to the offence. I constantly doubted my actions and self-worth as a result. Living in anxiety and fear just became a way of life for my siblings and me.

Even though we had always gone to the Anglican Church (in fact, my father had a very important role there for eight years), ours was a religious home and not a Christian one. My father often used the Bible to justify what I can only describe as wicked acts. This was the warped version of religion that I grew up with.

I use the word 'religion' because I have come to know and understand that Christianity is a way of life which is doing our best to follow Christ's example of love for God and humanity. There was nothing like this in my home. For my siblings and me, home was a place of fear and anxiety on a level that I pray no child ever should experience. Unfortunately, we live in a broken world, and there are millions of children who for one reason or another do not have the security of a loving home free from fear and pain.

#

When I started attending a girls' secondary school, I was not like most of my childhood friends. I was happiest when I was at school. This was because of the horrible treatment at the hands of my father. I hated Friday afternoons just like I hated the end of each school day. I knew that I would be going back to the prison I called home. As it got closer to the end of each school day, the stomach churning and anxiety would start as I faced going home with growing dread.

This wonderful place called school was where I knew I could be myself – even though there were things I was plainly useless at, i.e. all forms of sport and physical activity. My physical education teachers had to give up on me because my coordination was non-existent. I dropped balls all the time and was the last in every race.

The one thing that I loved apart from my schoolwork (I was a regular swot) was singing. Singing was my only escape from many childhood troubles and the pain of being abused at home. My mum (a pure soprano whose voice would rival that of a professional opera singer) used to teach us old hymns of the Anglican Church whenever she had the opportunity to – when my father was out.

I was not allowed to go to church choir rehearsals. That would have given me a freedom that went against the ethos in which I was raised. I was able to participate in the school choir because the rehearsals took place during lunch breaks and it did not impact my studies. I was surprised that I was allowed to join.

I knew I could sing and forget about anything that was going on in my life. This would prove to be a saving grace when things got exceptionally difficult. The rehearsals took place in the chapel, and it was the one building that every student treated with respect and reverence. As soon as the bell rang, you would see girls rushing from different parts of the school and chattering away. However, once we got to the front of the chapel, all talking stopped like a tap had been turned off. We would then enter in an orderly fashion, and each girl would take her place in one of the four parts: soprano, alto, tenor, or bass (it was particularly fascinating to my 10-year-old self how low some girls could sing).

Whenever I had the opportunity to do so, I would go into the chapel before everyone else and start singing the hymns my mum taught us at home. Sometimes one of the choirmasters would accompany me on the organ. I would feel transported away from all problems – no fear, no anxiety, no pain. I sang in that choir for six years and without a doubt, it was one of the highlights of my school days.

2

The Tidal Wave Hits

'When the tidal wave of trauma hits, your narrative is forever changed.'

– Bamidele Adenipekun

My mum was diagnosed with breast cancer when I was 13 years old. We were living in Nigeria at that time. I had a 12-year-old brother called Kayode, a 7-year-old sister called Tokunbo, and a 4-year-old sister called Adekemi (my older sister Titi was still in the UK). Dealing with cancer in a happy home is devastating enough. In an abusive and dysfunctional home, the situation is just made worse. Because of my father, there was no discussion, no explanation – just tense silence that was unlike anything we had lived through up to that point. The fear and anxiety became worse than what we had previously known.

I for one knew that something was seriously wrong, but I was not allowed to ask about it. All I could do was walk around the house on eggshells, afraid to rock the boat. There were whispered discussions between my parents as well as between my mum and one of my aunts. As soon as any of us children entered the room, discussions stopped.

After she was diagnosed with this cancer, my mum had a long consultation with our family doctor in the town where we lived. My mum came back home stating that she had been referred to the teaching hospital, which was 3–4 hours' drive away. Initially, I thought that she would be back in the next day or two.

My mum was away from home for six weeks. An older cousin came to stay with us for a few weeks to show me the ropes so that I could run the house whilst my parents were away. My father would leave home first thing in the morning and come back very late at night, angrier and sadder than I had ever seen him. His anger, of course, was manifested in rages at what he saw as my ineptitude in managing the household properly. Given the fact that I was 13 years old, one would think that I might have been cut some slack for not being a superb homemaker.

Such rational thinking never featured in my father's reasoning. My mother's illness just made him meaner. After six weeks, my mum came home, but she was not the same person that had left. For starters, she was not as strong as she had been before her hospital stay. For weeks after she returned, I wondered what the problem was as no information was forthcoming from the adults. I decided to take matters into my own hands. I sneaked a peek into where she kept her new set of drugs (she seemed to have an awful lot of them, about six different types).

I opened one of them – Tamoxifen – and took out the drug information sheet. It stated that the drug was for the treatment of breast cancer. At the time, all I knew was that it must be bad for my mum to have lost one of her breasts. There was no-one I could ask for information, and I surely did not want to cause my mum any more pain by asking difficult questions.

#

To provide context for the situation, the health care system in Nigeria at that time was deplorable at best. It still is. Nigeria in the early 1990s was an environment where there were gross systemic failures, which meant very little investment in infrastructure, and everyone suffered as a result. All forms of care for basic human needs were lacking. There was a lack of constant electric power both in homes and at institutions, no running water in lots of homes, a prevalence of poor roads, and a general absence of decent socioeconomic infrastructures.

Nowhere was this poverty more glaring than within the health care system. In 1991, the population of the city where we lived was over 150,000. There were two relatively large hospitals as well as a few other private clinics. However, none of them had any facilities whatsoever to make an initial cancer diagnosis or support patients in any way, shape, or form. There were times when, for a couple of days at least, none of the X-ray machines at the hospitals were in working order. There was also the issue of medical negligence and/or misconduct which was *never* addressed. Unfortunately, that remains the case today in Nigeria and most sub-Saharan African countries.

#

There was a general lack of awareness about the cancer epidemic at the time. This lack of awareness was, arguably, not exclusive to Africa in those days. It is a sad reality that in an atmosphere of ignorance, myths and superstitions abound to the detriment of the society. In those days, many attributed an illness like breast cancer to the workings of wickedness and evil spirits, adding a layer of stigma to already traumatic circumstances. Even well-educated people like my father (who had spent over a decade in the UK) subconsciously bought into the falsehood, indirectly blaming the patient for some perceived wrongdoing which had brought on such a dreadful disease.

As my mother was already isolated due to domestic abuse, cancer diagnosis further exacerbated the exclusion she must have felt. The only times she had visitors was when my father was not at home, and this was limited to a couple of neighbours who came to encourage her and pray with her. These instances were so few and far between that they might have been non-existent. With the benefit of hindsight, openness to others was not even a consideration in an abusive context. However, as children growing up in that environment, my siblings and I lived in such a heightened state of dread and anxiety that it was grim even by our previous standards.

3

Life Comes Unglued

'To not have your suffering recognised is an almost unbearable form of violence.'

– Andrei Lankov

In my teenage wisdom, I thought that if I could get the household running properly without causing my parents any worry, things would settle and return to normal. Little did I realise that this was the 'new normal'. Life would never be the same again.

After recovering from the surgery, my mum underwent 13 months of radiotherapy, commuting on a weekly basis and only returning home on weekends. After the hospital treatments, she appeared to regain some of her strength. She was still taking her drugs, but apart from quarterly appointments at the hospital, it seemed that we would get my mum back.

Nine months after her last radiotherapy treatment, my mum pulled what she thought was a muscle in her right leg and started limping around the house. Again, she went to see our family doctor, who advised her to tell her oncologist and demand X-rays before coming to any conclusions. Through a catalogue of errors and gross incompetence on the part of the oncologist she saw (who was not her usual one), my mum was given medication for arthritis and asked to return in three months.

Needless to say, her condition worsened over the next month. She lost all sensation in her right leg. In desperation, my mum returned to the hospital where the requisite X-rays, scans, and tests were then carried out. The diagnosis was bleak. It was cancer again! This time, the cancer had spread to her bone marrow and was making the rounds throughout her entire body. She lost the use of both her legs and was unable to attend to her personal care needs. She began more aggressive treatments than ever before. In the last 15 months of her life, my mum was hospitalised five times.

#

I was my mother's full-time caregiver whenever she was at home. My father's reaction to her illness was bizarre, or so I thought at the time. He had always been verbally and physically abusive; that was a given. But he became angrier. Nothing my siblings and I did was ever right. However, as the primary caregiver, I was the focus of the worst of his rages. In hindsight, I think his attitude was a mixture of fear, paranoia, and deep-seated anger.

None of my siblings were allowed in her room in case they caught whatever infection or disease he stated she was riddled with. That was his view of the cancer patient– one to be kept from view and contact. I find it ironic now that he had no qualms whatsoever about me being exposed to anything. He could not stand the smell in her bedroom, so he would come into the room whilst I was attending to her personal care and liberally spray air freshener, complaining about the 'smell' in the room. The sicker my mum got, the angrier he got, and he took his anger out on us.

More than anything else, I wanted to take away the pain that this caused my mum. I had never felt so helpless. Until my mum became ill, we were not close. I was angry at her for her inability to defend us from my father's abuse. However, in the final 15 months of her life, we became very close. She shared so much with me for which I am immensely grateful.

You see, as a 16–17-year-old (who had grown up fast in the last couple of years), I was able to listen and understand my parents better as individuals and as a couple. In terms of conduct and characteristics, my father has the hallmarks of a narcissist and a sociopath. In his earlier years, he was able to cover that with charm and charisma as many abusers do. My mum was naïve prior to meeting my father, having only known the adoration of her own father. Therefore, she was ripe for the picking. This assessment of my parents' relationship is in no way a dishonourable one. It is just a summary of the facts as I see them.

#

In those last months, my mum told me all I needed to know about her – warts and all. She did not shy away from difficult revelations, no matter how bad they made her look. It was at this point that she gave me the details about the cancer and her treatment – some of which I shared above.

When my mum became ill, some Christian friends of hers came to visit, and she gave her life to Christ. She would go on to renew her faith and commitment before she died. Throughout my mum's illness, her Bible and books to boost her faith were her constant companions. Her other solace was singing. Neighbours used to stop to listen whenever we sang hymns together as a family. This love of singing through any and every season was a wonderful lesson that I picked up, and it has carried me through. You see, I realised even then that I could express all that I was feeling by using the words of faithful Christians who had endured even bigger trials than I could begin to comprehend.

As a result of her faith, my mum went through a harrowing, painful, and debilitating experience with such grace and kindness that it's special just to think about it, even after all this time. There were a couple of women in the neighbourhood who were going through tough times. As ill as my mum was, she would invite them into her bedroom (whilst my father was out, of course), pray with them, share her food, and counsel them. If she was awake, she would always make time for someone in need. However, I have to say that I was the principal recipient of her kindness, wisdom, and grace in the final phase of her life.

#

Finally, at the age of 46, her body had enough. She passed away in hospital, six days before Christmas. When my siblings and I were given the news, my first feeling was one of relief. I knew she was no longer in pain. Even though my relationship with God was not on a solid footing, I knew my mum had gone home to be with her Lord because she lived so close to Him and let her light shine.

The adults finalised funeral arrangements; she was buried four days after she died so as not to disrupt the Christmas services at the church. As we only found out about her death two days after the event, there was hardly any breathing space before the funeral.

The days and months that followed were surreal, to say the least. Well-meaning friends and acquaintances were mainly concerned about how my father would cope with the loss of his wife. As the oldest sibling living at home, the instructions to look after my father came at me constantly, which I found hurtful. I remember wondering why the adults felt that only my father suffered the loss and why children's grief was not acknowledged in any way.

#

I cannot tell which was more devastating to my mind as a child: the illness or the fact that no-one provided us, the children, with any tangible information. How does one manage day-to-day realities with children who have to watch a parent battle serious illness? This is a seriously sticky issue – after all, the effects of the illness may become a new normal for the children as well as the adults.

I know that loving parents want the best for their children and will seek to do all in their power to protect them from pain or harm. However, there are some pains that must be exposed early to reduce their overwhelming effects. I cannot speak for why my father kept information away from us, but I think my mother would have wanted to spare us the pain of knowing how bad her health situation was at the initial diagnosis stage.

However, it is possible to do more harm than good in the long run when there is a lack of openness. I cannot claim to know what went on in the minds of my siblings at the time, but a fair assessment of our home's atmosphere would be one of helplessness, bewilderment, and plain old confusion.

I have come to know from experience that children have deep feelings, especially in situations where they have to watch a parent become critically ill. When such feelings are not acknowledged, the children are devalued and disempowered in ways that I think adults would find astounding. As a parent, I do acknowledge that I have the inherent instinct of wanting to protect my child from unpleasant situations. However, the reality is that when there is a diagnosis of serious illness (be it cancer or any other disease), there is no hiding from the unpleasantness of certain symptoms and the side effects of gruelling treatment regimens.

I wish I could go back and tell my teenage self that her feelings mattered and were worthy of consideration. I wish she could have been given information about breast cancer at the very beginning and in a way that would have pulled the family together to support her mother better, pulling down the 'bogeyman' effect.

I implore *all* parents of young children or teenagers who have been given a diagnosis of cancer or other serious illness to please involve them as soon as possible.

The level of involvement will be different in each situation; after all, no-one knows children better than their parents. It can be anything from telling them that their mum or dad will have to go to hospital because they are unwell to gently preparing them for significant changes that might occur. I appreciate that a diagnosis of serious illness can knock you for six (especially if there was no warning), but thinking that children cannot pick up on the tension or vibes around them is just unrealistic.

In today's wonderful age of the internet, there will always be avenues to go to for support and information. The plethora of information can be a disadvantage, though, if children are not given the necessary filters that will make their own family situation more manageable. It is better for your children to get the facts as they apply to your situation and how you intend to proceed before they get more than they bargained for on some unregulated chat forums.

I am a firm believer in asking for help if you need it – so if you want extra sources of reliable information and support for children, ask medical professionals and associations that have a track record of providing this.

#

On the 23rd anniversary of my mum's death, as I thought about her, I could not help writing a poem in her memory. Here it goes:

Our Songbird

Songbird, lift up your head and sing;
Those beautiful notes were meant to soar.
The day our songbird was silenced for good,
The other creatures of the forest waited and waited
Because they thought that for certain
Those notes that reached a crescendo, no matter how gloomy the sky,
Surely, they will resound soon enough
And the forest will again be bathed in their beauty,
Sounds so sublime you could be forgiven
For thinking that it was bequeathed by the heavenly chorus.

The Creator however declared, I have need of her.
My dear songbird, it is time to come home.
Trampled upon and crushed was never what I fashioned you for.
In spite of those circumstances,
Your voice still soared.
Now I want you in My courts
To behold and worship Me for eternity.
Your earthly legacy will not be dimmed in any way.
Welcome home,
My beloved, the welcome party and your mansion awaits.

4

Escape from Prison

*'Home is not where you are born: home is where all
your attempts to escape cease.'*

– Naguib Mahfouz

Life after my mother's death was bleak, to say the least.
It felt as if someone had just snuffed out the lone candle
providing light in that dark house. When I gained admission
into the same university that my brother was in, I
felt relief mixed with a guilt that I would carry for years.
The relief that I had a reprieve from my father's abuse
was tinged with guilt for leaving my two younger sisters
behind.

But going to university did not stop the abuse or the
impossible demands. My father would withhold money
that my brother and I required for living expenses to ensure
that we came home every two or three weeks. I remember
thinking that it would be years before my degree ended
and I could escape his cruelty for good.

Help came from a most unexpected quarter. My big
sister, who had lived away from the family in the UK, was

able to get in touch and visit. I cannot begin to imagine how she must have felt to find out about mum's death more than a year after the fact. Her opportunity to reconnect with our mother after years of separation was gone forever. Despite the difficult circumstances and years of separation, she managed to convince our father to allow my brother and me to go to the UK.

As my father thought we were only travelling to the UK for a holiday and would be buying everything on his shopping list, he agreed. It is ironic that because of my father's two basest motivations – pride and greed – my brother and I got freedom from his cruelty more quickly than we could ever have imagined. I am very grateful.

#

As all victims of abuse know, physical separation does not mean instant mental and psychological freedom. When your father has told you for years that you are inferior and of subhuman intellect, the feelings of inadequacy and deep-seated self-loathing plague you until there is a permanent shift in your perspective.

Throughout my studies in Nigeria, I worked extremely hard to get the best grades possible, but my father was never satisfied. I mostly got straight As, but the odd Bs and Cs on my end-of-term report were guaranteed to earn me a good beating.

At the age of 11, I reached a point where I felt that life was not worth living and it would be better for everyone if I were out of the picture. In my naïve young mind, I thought that by ingesting a strong disinfectant with a poison warning, I could just quietly fade away in my sleep. My brother and a cousin, who were present at the time, managed to talk me out of drinking the unpleasant stuff. They reminded me that if anything happened to me, my father would put the blame squarely at their feet. I did not want to get them in trouble, and that ended that desperate thought.

The damaging effects of growing up in an abusive environment went on to manifest themselves in various ways in my life for years. For example, victims of abuse are especially adept at wearing masks. Mine was an elaborate façade of confidence and intelligence that was at odds with what was going on in my mind. I brought some serious baggage with me to the UK, and it required consistent renewing of my thinking before I felt like I was worth anything. It took about 18 months of standing in front of the mirror every morning and telling myself that I was not inferior and deficient before the message finally began to sink in.

There is an institutional mindset that comes from being imprisoned for an extended period. That mindset must be broken for ex-inmates to have a sense of normalcy in the outside world. A failure to deal with this will most likely result in future stints of imprisonment and/or self-destructive behaviour.

I struggled with the issue of what to do with my life. When I was in the prison of my childhood home, I had no say whatsoever about which subjects I would study and what profession I would eventually pursue. In some ways, this reflected the African culture of 'your parents know best and you do as you are told'. My authoritarian father carried it to an extreme in what I can only describe as a living nightmare, forcing me to take a course of study that I was intellectually unsuited for – Applied Geophysics.

Upon arriving in the UK with my big sister, I was desperate to start studying again and make a success of my life. However, I still held onto the damaging notion that unless I studied something in the 'pure sciences,' I was stupid. This resulted in me spending four years studying and failing at various subjects that were not right for me. The irony was that quite a few of my friends at the time used to tell me how intelligent I was. But because my grades did not reflect their views, I figured that their friendly biases skewed their judgement. With each failed study attempt, I had to fight off the refrains from my childhood about being inferior.

One might think that since I was out of the oppressive environment, I would make the right decision about what to study. Unless you have been a victim of abuse, you cannot begin to comprehend what a herculean task self-discovery and self-acceptance is. The journey is by no means a short or straightforward one.

#

Once my father realised that we had escaped from his terror, he quickly figured out how he could work things out to his own advantage. He knew which buttons to push, and he did so with ease. And so began the emotional blackmail.

As he was not gainfully employed, he began demanding money for living expenses. This was a habit he had got into during the early days of his marriage to my mum; he just never got out of it.

He knew that concern for my two younger sisters, who were still in school at the time, meant that I would send whatever money I could spare. Therefore, I took on low-paid work whilst I was studying. The long work hours did not do my studies any favours.

In spite of the hard work, I was still relieved that my escape from my father was permanent. My only issue was that my sisters still had to live under his roof. Eventually, when they left home and went to their respective universities, the burden of guilt that I carried for not being there for them was eased completely.

#

One of the most important decisions that I made as a university student whilst in Nigeria was to become a true Christian. What I embraced was not the parody of religion that I saw my father practise but a close relationship with God. This has been the bedrock of my life and all I do since.

In the early days of my Christian walk, I had so many false starts and setbacks. My image of an earthly father was one of cruelty, and this coloured my view of God for a long time. I thought of Him as a harsh judge who was ready to knock me on the head for the slightest infraction. This, of course, is not the case.

Seven years down the line, I experienced God's love for the first time in such a tangible way that my analytical and critical mind could not dismiss it. This experience affirmed and validated me in ways I never thought possible. I now realise that this same faith is what sustained my mother in the final years of her life as she dealt with cancer and an abusive marriage.

Part II

Tough Call

5

A Rude Awakening

'The road of life twists and turns and no two directions are ever the same. Yet our lessons come from the journey, not the destination.'

– Don Williams Jr.

My mum died at age 46 after battling cancer for three years. I was 17 years old at the time. For the next seven years, cancer was just the disease that my mum had died of. I read up about it when 1 was doing A-level biology, and I did my own preliminary reading on how this rogue illness develops and how it ends up becoming a monster that wreaks so much havoc on the human body. I was young (hey, I am still young!), so I did not think much about it. As far as I knew, before my mum, my family had no history of cancer.

My first rude awakening came when I was a 23-year-old university student in London. I felt a couple of lumps in my left breast. Stomach-churning time – my mum's cancer started in her left breast and the nearby lymph nodes. I told myself that I would just go to my GP, she would dismiss my concerns, and life could then proceed as normal.

It was April or May 2000. I went by myself. I did not tell anyone because, after all, I would be sent off on my merry way. Wrong, wrong, wrong.

After the doctor finished her examination, she stated that she would refer me to what was then the Elizabeth Garrett Anderson Women's Hospital. I asked her why she felt the need to refer someone as young as I, and her response was something that I would hear quite a few times in the coming years. 'With your family history, let's be on the safe side and check.' I remember sitting in the waiting area of the hospital thinking that this must be a bad dream. I was in my early 20s, for crying out loud! In the waiting area, I saw only women who were decades older than me, and I just wanted someone to tell me that there had been a mistake.

After the scans and biopsies were complete, I had to wait quite a few weeks for my results due to the huge backlogs in London at that time. I took my second-year exams at university, which I royally flunked as I could not think or function whilst waiting for the results. It did not even occur to me to notify the University Board and ask to take time off. I figured that I should be able to deal with it. After all, people dealt with worse things daily. No use whining.

But I did pray as I had never prayed before – with expectation – because when all was said and done, I could not do anything else. In His infinite mercy, the Father heard my cry, and the tests results said that the lumps were benign, though I had to undergo surgery to have them removed. After the surgery, the surgeon was pleased to let me know that I would not have an unsightly scar; he sure was pleased with his 'needlework.' I was told that

I should not have any further problems. Phew! I was so relieved. I praised the Lord for that testimony for months.

However, the rollercoaster ride of that year was not over yet. My periods stopped for several months. I was relieved because I used to have painful periods and I thought *good riddance*. Oh, the folly of youth! When I look back now, I wish I could shake my 24-year-old self and tell her to ask for help – stop pretending to be super-woman. 16 years later, I am only just beginning to learn that lesson. Better late than never, I say....

I did speak to an older friend, and she told me in no uncertain terms that 14 months was too long to be un-concerned about the cessation of my periods. Your eyes are not playing tricks on you – yes, one year and two months!

I went back to my GP. She shook her head when I told her I was only seeing her to get my older friend off my back. She referred me to get a scan, and I was diag-nosed with polycystic ovary syndrome. My GP prescribed a contraceptive pill to see if that would kick-start false periods. She also gave me the contact details of a women's health group that knew more about the condition and its potential impact on my fertility and general well-being.

Between the GP and the health group, I figured that none of them had a solution that I was prepared to live with. For the only time in my life, I did what felt best to me: I did not touch a single pill. Now, is that faith or foolishness? I will leave you to decide. From where I was standing, the pill would only make me ill, bloated, or both. Why put myself through the hassle if it would not correct my ovaries?

I would not advise anyone to follow my example. For me, though, I felt that was the only decision that made sense. In desperation, I cried out to God, and He healed me. Less than three weeks later, my periods returned in full force at a most unexpected moment.

I had just left a church service where I had thankfully been able to forget all that I was going through; I just praised and worshipped the Father with abandon. From that point onwards, my periods became frighteningly regular for the first time in my life. When I finally went back to another GP for an unrelated issue, she looked at my notes and wanted to know why I had not followed medical advice. I just told her that I no longer required medical intervention because I already had my miracle. She looked at me as if I had lost my marbles, but I was not perturbed. I had another scan about two years later. They searched very thoroughly for the cysts in both ovaries, but they found no trace. The scan was repeated, but the result remained the same.

At this juncture, you might wonder what motivated my decision. Was it faith, foolishness, or presumption? You get to decide. All I know is that *all* the glory belongs to my heavenly Father, Maker of Heaven and Earth. Medical science was not responsible for this miracle. To Him be praise, glory, and honour forever.

As you will discover later in this book, no two experiences of trials are ever the same. This is particularly true for illness and divine healing. My personal belief, which is grounded in my faith in God and His Word, does not change no matter what circumstance of life I face.

6

Motherhood Surprise

'He who is without sin among you, let him throw a stone at her first.'

— John 8:7

In the years between 2000 and 2002, I began to grow in my Christian walk and give more thought to what my purpose was, as opposed to just studying with a view to getting a prestigious job at the end of it. The more I learnt and grew, the more I realised I had a passion for fighting injustice and being a voice for the voiceless. I remember watching the news, seeing the suffering of people displaced by conflict, and being nearly moved to tears. This experience gave me a heart for missions.

I communicated this desire to my church leadership at the time. They very graciously sponsored my trip to Thailand in 2002 under the auspices of Tearfund, a UK-based Christian relief organisation. It was a 6-week trip as part of a team of 13, and it stood out as one of the most rewarding experiences of my life up to that point. The work in Thailand involved two local charities: one that worked with disabled children and adults, and the other with families affected by HIV/AIDS, which was at its peak in the country at the time and left behind orphans to be cared for by elderly relatives. One thing was clear to me. I realised that despite my previous life experiences, I was quite fortunate not to be in those circumstances.

On my return to the UK, there was a disconnect between most of my friends and me at the time. That was understandable, as they did not see or experience what I did. As the months went by, I suppose I got disillusioned with my ability to effect lasting change on the vast ills and inequalities of the world in general. I decided to set aside the whole missions idea and do my own thing. It was not so much a grand statement as something that I stumbled away from.

#

2003 was a momentous year. I completed my first degree and got pregnant with Amy whilst being unmarried. This could be deemed a huge fall from grace.

There is no doubt that it was a big stumble, one which I thought would end my walk with God for certain. However, it became my biggest lesson in the grace and forgiveness of the Father. As I sought and accepted His pardon, I also started a journey of getting to know Him on a deeper level than ever before.

There are different types of people in the church: the pious and gracious, the pious and judgemental, and all shades in-between. My biggest blessings at the time were just a handful of friends and my pastors who categorically told those without sin to cast the first stone.

Life as I knew it had changed forever. If anyone had told me a year before that I would be in that position, I would have dismissed the idea as nonsense.

Once I got over the shock of being pregnant, I realised that I had been given a priceless gift, one I did not think I would have had without medical intervention. For the first 10–11 weeks, it was a textbook pregnancy – nausea, exhaustion – nothing out of the ordinary. However, from week 12, my skin went berserk. Six weeks and five specialists later, it turned out that I had a severe case of pregnancy-induced eczema. The dermatologist stated she had never seen anything like it in her 20 years of practice and asked for permission to take before and after treatment photographs. I was prescribed strong topical steroids as well as all sorts of emollients and oils. This was all closely monitored at fortnightly appointments with the dermatologist and obstetrician.

At about 24 weeks, when I was alone at home, I woke up to find the chest area of my nightgown soaked with blood. I was shocked beyond belief. I then discovered that the blood came from my breasts. After praying and cleaning myself up, I figured that it was probably a result of the eczema, which at the time had caused the whole surface of my skin to peel, with my palms bleeding in the initial stages.

Over the next couple of weeks, there was a repeat of this, but I figured there was no use panicking as it was not life-threatening or painful. *Duh!* It did not even occur to me to call my midwife or tell a friend at this stage. Looking back now, it was just the grace of God that sustained me. The unusual bleeding was the least of my worries at the time. My scans and blood tests were normal, so my focus was on work, getting a secure tenancy, and buying the essential nursery items.

#

This attitude of taking everything on the chin was about to be tested to its limits. At week 30, I was at work feeling unwell. A couple of colleagues took me to a nearby hospital, and I was monitored for a short while. Everything appeared to be okay, but the attending physician told me to ask my obstetrician to conduct a more detailed internal exam at my next appointment, which was in the next couple of days. At my scheduled appointment, preliminary tests appeared all right, but the internal exam was a different story altogether. When my obstetrician completed her examination, she took off her gloves and calmly told me that the membrane surrounding my baby appeared to have ruptured.

What she was saying did not even register; I was mentally reviewing my nursery shopping list and thinking about how quickly I could tidy up loose ends at work. The obstetrician then told me to go home, pack a bag, and be back in hospital within the next couple of hours. She also placed a call to the maternity ward to make a bed available for me straightaway.

Even at this stage, I was not concerned at all. Maybe if someone else had been with me, they would have impressed upon me how serious the doctor was. Instead, I was arguing with her because all I could see was my carefully laid plans turned upside down. Needless to say, I was not amused. When the doctor realised she was not getting through to me, she told me that she was not giving me a choice. I had to return within a couple of hours and stay in hospital.

As I settled into the hospital ward a few hours later, I realised that this was more than just an inconvenience – there were major concerns about my unborn baby. I was monitored every hour for the rest of the night. It goes without saying that I did not get much sleep.

In the midst of all this, a peace that is difficult to describe enveloped me. I used to be a worrier, from the time I was a child. The Father, of course, knew this about me all the way through. That is why the gift of His peace is not one I could ever take for granted. At a time when others' hearts would have been failing them for fear, I was calm and serene knowing *all is well*. If anyone had asked me to articulate how I knew that, I doubt I could have given a coherent response. But I was certain of one thing: my heavenly Father was with me all the way through. Therefore, fear would not overwhelm me.

When a scan was done the following morning, it was discovered that I had lost a lot of amniotic fluid. I was given steroid injections to help mature my baby's lungs in case delivery had to happen within the next couple of days. Over the next four to five days, I was monitored to check for any signs of early labour, but it was not to be. The decision was then made that since labour was not imminent, if possible, my baby would be kept inside until 36 weeks, after which time the birth would either be induced or completed via caesarean section.

During this hospital admission, the problem with my breasts raised its ugly head again. I woke up in the middle of the night to discover that the front of my nightgown was soaked in blood. As I knew the source of the mess this time, I went straight to show the nurses on duty. Even now, I cannot forget the shock of one of the older nurses. I realised that, to someone else, I must have looked a sight. As calmly as I could, I explained to her that this was not the first occurrence. The following day, I received a visit from one of the breast surgeons who told me that as I was pregnant, there was not much that could be done. I was instructed to get back in touch with the breast clinic after delivery.

After just over two weeks in hospital, it was deemed that there was nothing to be gained by keeping me there. I was required to go to the Maternity Day Unit every other day for monitoring, just to be sure that nothing untoward cropped up again.

#

The first monitoring session went okay. Not so, two days later. For more than an hour, there was no reading showing for my baby's heartbeat. When the sheet was printed, the space where her heart tracing was supposed to be was blank. I was 34 weeks pregnant.

The midwife on duty stated she had no choice but to transfer me to the labour ward and page my obstetrician. During all this, my overriding thought was that the Father had got me through thus far, and He surely would not leave nor forsake me. This sense of calm and peace was the biggest blessing in the coming hours, as it was then discovered that my baby's heart rate was irregular and slowing down. My sister who was with me was worried, but did her best not to show it. My brother came to join us over the course of the day. I was so glad not to have been alone during those hours of waiting on what decision my doctor would make. An emergency C-section was then scheduled, with a paediatrician in attendance. Due to unforeseen circumstances, the surgery itself was delayed by about three hours, by which time my sister and brother had left. It just happened that a midwife on duty that night volunteered to stay with me throughout the birth.

Even though I was in pain, there were no words to describe my sense of wonder and overwhelming love for this child I had carried for 8 months. As the baby's sex could not be determined during the scans, once I realised

I had a girl, her first name was already decided – Amy, meaning dearly loved. Given my own childhood experience, I wanted Amy to know how I felt about her from the beginning of her life.

After all the post-birth checks were complete, the doctors left Amy and me in a recovery room for a couple of hours. I was in so much pain at the time that I could not hold my baby. Whilst in the recovery room, the same midwife who had attended the birth gave my baby her bottle and kept monitoring her. After about an hour or less, the midwife said she was concerned about my baby's breathing. Bearing in mind the amount of pain I was in, I just figured the midwife was being melodramatic.

Thank God for a dedicated and caring midwife – she did not listen to me. She paged the paediatrician, and within the next 10–15 minutes there was chaos. All I knew was that I was wheeled out of the room and a resuscitation cart was brought in for my baby. At that point, I was alarmed, because about half an hour passed (it felt like a lifetime) before I was apprised of the situation. All I could do was pray and ask for God's hand to rest on my child. In that lonely room where there was no human comfort or support, I cried out to God, and He heard my cry. What a wonderful Father and Saviour He is!

Eventually, the attending doctor came to tell me that Amy went into respiratory distress and would have died if that midwife had not raised the alarm quickly. Wow! This midwife took special care of Amy and me because I was on my own. If my family had been around, she would have gone back to the labour ward as soon as my baby was delivered. God, who knows the end from the beginning, knew that only a dedicated professional would have been vigilant enough. Amy was placed on a ventilator and sent to the neonatal unit for premature babies where she remained for the next 19 days.

Meanwhile, I was sent off to the main maternity ward. The day after the birth, when I could get out of bed, I got a message from the neonatal unit to send expressed breast milk for Amy. Whilst using the breast pump, I discovered that there was blood mixed with the milk. It was like two ducts opened: one with milk and the other with fresh blood. If I had breastfed my baby directly, I probably would not have noticed anything untoward for quite a while. I cannot even begin to imagine what that would have been like for her delicate stomach. The neonatal nurses decided that because of the blood content, my breast milk could not be used.

I then had to go back to the breast surgeons, this time for extensive testing to determine the source of the blood in my breasts. Eventually, the right breast settled down, but the left one remained a problem. The source of the blood was a cyst which, after it had been drained, would disappear and then show up a week later. After the third draining, the cyst became a dense, solid mass.

Scans and biopsies later revealed it to be another benign growth, and this was surgically removed when Amy was 11 months old. I must say that the second breast surgeon was in no way as meticulous as the first. I ended up with a horrible jagged scar, which I was seriously displeased with for a long time. Without the prayers and support of my pastors and church at the time, I do not know how I would have survived that time without cracking up.

#

With prayers and the Word of God, I began to learn how to contend for my healing and keep trusting the Father in spite of untoward circumstances. I prayed not just for my healing but for everyday life as a single parent. I knew beyond the shadow of a doubt that if I did not have the direction of the Holy Spirit, I would fail as a mother. As every parent will testify, babies do not come with a set of written instructions. It is only by leaning on the Holy Spirit and getting to understand from the Word of God that each parent can successfully navigate the parenting journey.

There is no doubt that in life, there will be mistakes aplenty. Nowhere will this be more evident than in the case of a single parent. You know the buck stops with you, and you are constantly trying to wear two hats at the same time. I can testify and categorically state that nothing worked better for me than prayers.

I believe that no detail of Amy's life – present or future – is too big or too small to commend to the Father's hands. To the glory of His name, He has never, ever failed me. Whether I am in a busy A&E department due to a health crisis or dealing with naughty behaviour, the Father proves Himself to be faithful and all-powerful repeatedly.

After the second breast surgery, I thought I was home free. Apart from the unsightly scar (which, in my vanity, I would get cross about from time to time), life could proceed on an even keel again.

7

The Monster Comes Calling Again

'The expected is what keeps us steady. It's the unexpected that changes our lives forever.'

— Shonda Rhimes

In the following year, I became dissatisfied with my walk with God. I knew there had to be more; I wanted a deeper level of intimacy with Him. The desire for deeper intimacy was not new. From my early days of being a Christian, I would listen to or read about people whose intimate walk with God I desperately craved. I was plain tired of coasting along.

I knew there were barriers in my heart and mind that had to come down first. Up till that point, there were certain gifts of the Spirit that my analytical mind was sceptical of. Some of these included Word of knowledge, prophecy, and Word of wisdom. You see, I used to think that these were products of people's imaginations and deemed them unreliable at best.

Part of this journey of self-awareness was to acknowledge that my default mode was panic and anxiety at that time. This became more pronounced after I became a mother. In those first couple of months of Amy's life, I worried constantly about not being a good parent, as I did not have stellar examples growing up. I also beat myself up for short-changing Amy by not being married, thereby bringing her into the world with an absentee father.

Nothing, however, could dim my love for this loving heavenly Father of mine, so I figured I would just talk to Him about all these thoughts running through my head. One of the first things I noticed was the change in the kind of prayers I offered. I acknowledged my inability to pray aright without the Holy Spirit, so when I invited Him to help me pray, things were bound to be different.

Now here's a note of caution: be careful what you pray for....

Once I started praying about being a living sacrifice and totally consecrating myself, things got serious quickly. I realise that in contemporary Christianity, matters such as these are not that popular. Part of the reason is that it means death to our flesh. It felt like a spotlight had turned on inside my heart. My innermost desires, motives, and thoughts I now had to examine in the light of the truth of God's Word. When Jesus was praying for His disciples in John 17:17, He said, 'Sanctify them by Your truth, Your word is truth.'

It was crunch time. Time to stop paying lip service to God. Time to make a stand for what I professed to believe. I realised that I was holding on too tightly to certain things, to the point where I exalted them above God in my life.

Our heavenly Father is so loving and so kind. Part of His expression of love towards us is loading us with benefits. I believe that having children to love, whether biological or adopted, is one of the most precious gifts we have. I cannot speak for anyone else, but I must admit that it was not difficult for my love for her to take pride of place in my heart above my love for God. Until I got into this season of wanting more of God, I was blind to my idolatry.

I realised then that the notion that I could keep Amy safe and preserve her from all harm was a folly of epic proportions. At this juncture, I realised afresh how difficult it must have been for Abraham to have obeyed God's Word to go and sacrifice his son. I sure cannot speak for Abraham, but I can say that for me, I could not have surrendered Amy totally to God without the help of the Holy Spirit.

I need to stress that it took me quite a while to get to that point of surrender, and without a doubt, it was one of the most difficult decisions of my life. Once I surrendered though, it felt as if a huge burden was lifted from my shoulders. You see, it was only then that I realised that there was no need to fret or be anxious. My child was now totally God's, and it was His responsibility to preserve her and perfect all that concerns her. From that time to date, where Amy is concerned, my default mode is no longer panic or anxiety but a deep-seated assurance in the Father who watches over her always.

Before seeking a deeper relationship with the Father, I was like the children of Israel: more acquainted with His works than His ways. I certainly acknowledge His works, as He has been so gracious to me, but focussing on His acts alone gives me a limited view of who He is. The children of Israel saw God's mighty works but mostly missed out on the wonder of God Himself. At the time of the miraculous act, it was easy for them to be grateful and swept up in the celebration that followed. However, this only lasted until the next crisis, when fear overwhelmed them, and they wanted to return to Egypt.

I now had a deeper desire to know Him better and get to know and hear His voice – not how He spoke to someone else but how He would choose to speak to me as an individual.

The Father has a very good sense of humour. The spiritual gifts and manifestations that I had hitherto turned my nose up at were now revealed to me in ways that I would never be able to dismiss again. In the posture of surrender, neither hardness of heart nor selfish ambition has a place. Needless to say, my pride had to take a backseat. This was a season of stretching, the likes of which I had hitherto not encountered.

#

Within a year, I had responded to the call of God to move from London to Wales. As my relationship with God deepened, I became dissatisfied with where I was at in my life. With my first degree behind me, I needed to know what was next. After a lot of prayer and soul-searching, I knew the Master's programme in Wales was the one for me so I put in my application.

At that time, I could not accurately locate Wales on a map, let alone know how I was going to live there. Through a series of divine incidents, I got the provision I needed and support as required. I made a renewed commitment to the Lord to obey Him as He enabled me. The Father gave me His word that 'His grace is sufficient for all my needs' (2 Corinthians 12:9).

The thought of moving from everything familiar to a place where I did not know a soul, was overwhelming to say the least. The more I prayed, the clearer my path became. I was then able to make to-do lists and follow through on practical steps that I needed to take. Contrary to the deep and mysterious instructions that I expected, the guidance I got was on things like looking for and applying for sources of funding to cover part of my Master's tuition. I also looked for and found a nursery place for Amy. This was a profound lesson to me that instead of waiting forever for a lightning bolt of divine revelation; being diligent and faithful with what has been placed in my hand often paves the path to where I am meant to be.

The unvarnished truth is that God knows me through and through; He knows what I can handle and what will be beyond me. I think that we Christians would save ourselves a whole lot of hassle if we accepted the truth that our heavenly Father has the most in-depth knowledge of every single one of us. We can therefore give Him our total trust concerning the direction of our lives.

> 'O Lord, You have searched me and known me. You know my sitting down and my rising up; You understand my thought afar off. You comprehend my path and my lying down and are acquainted with all my ways. For there is not a word on my tongue, but behold O Lord You know it altogether. You have hedged me behind and before, and laid Your hand upon me. Such knowledge is too wonderful for me; it is high I cannot attain it.'
>
> – Psalm 139: 1–6 (NKJV)

That passage blows my mind every time I read it. The knowledge that this powerful, all-knowing God is my Maker, Lord, and Father I find most comforting. In a land where I did not know a soul, the Father surpassed my expectations. Every single need was met at the right time. Whether it was provision or grace to do all that I needed to, it was evident that the Father never left nor forsook Amy and me.

In our first eighteen months of living in Wales, I started and completed my Master's degree, and Amy started school. Despite the huge workload (working, studying, and single parenting), I was enabled not only to complete my degree but also to do an excellent job to the glory of the Father's name. It was undeniable that His all-sufficient grace was at work in every area of my life.

I will not lie – leaving behind my comfort zone in London was not a walk in the park, and I was tempted to cut tail and run. However, as the psalmist knew too well, trying to hide from God is an exercise in futility. Even when I am unfaithful, He remains ever faithful to His Word and His promises. Praise His name!

#

I could not have made the kind of choices I did in those years without putting my sole trust in God's Word. Little did I know how important this would be when I entered one of the darkest seasons I have ever lived through: the loss of a loved one in tragic circumstances.

That loss was so unexpected, and there were many unanswered questions. I know most people who suffer sudden loss can relate to the feeling of nearly drowning in unimaginable sorrow. If not for the grace of the Father and the assurance of His Word, I do not know what would have become of me.

As if this was not enough, the following month my big sister, Titi, was diagnosed with stage three aggressive breast cancer, which had metastasized to the lymph nodes.

Grrr! I had thought the spectre of that dodgy disease had gone from our lives forever. I could not have been more wrong. Over the course of five years, my sister would undergo extensive treatments, which included not only surgery, radiotherapy, and chemotherapy, but also gamma knife treatment and laser ablation. All the treatments – along with countless scans, blood tests, and other diagnostic procedures – took their toll on her body.

All throughout, Titi's strength and faith increased in ways that echoed our mum's journey two decades earlier. In both cases, there were crucial things missed by some doctors not just at the point of diagnosis but also over the course of treatment.

Watching a loved one suffer and go through such pain is an experience I never wanted to relive after my mother's death, and yet it appeared that history was repeating itself. At times like this, you feel so powerless that you could easily sink into a pit of despair from which it is difficult to climb out. I knew that to stay sane, I had to go to hide in my Refuge and Fortress – the Maker of Heaven and Earth with whom nothing is impossible. In any case, I knew we needed divine intervention.

Thank God for doctors and medical personnel, especially here in the U.K. For the most part, they apply their efforts and expertise to ensure the best possible outcomes for their patients. In no field is this more evident than in oncology. Between the clinicians and scientists, many advancements have been made, leading to higher survival rates and better prognoses for cancer patients over the last two decades.

However, it is clear that doctors can only give treatments. No matter how advanced – they cannot heal. The proof of the limitations of medical science advancements is in the sheer number of people who die despite, or because of, unwanted side effects from lethal drug combinations.

Only God can heal, and He is still in the healing business.

When I first heard about my sister's diagnosis, my first instinct was to fight. The battle with anxiety and doubt came later. The fighting instinct is one that I will forever be grateful for. When an enemy threatens someone close to you, I strongly believe that giving in is not a viable option. Otherwise, there is the risk of being crushed completely under the weight of despair.

Some can mistake a stand of faith for denial or burying one's head in the sand. There is a myriad of reasons for this, but I think the primary ones are unbelief and pity. For those who are not grounded in the efficacy of the Word of God and the promise of divine healing, it just does not stack up. As far as they are concerned, the person of faith is pitiable, since there is no other solution to deal with disease besides medical science.

There are two questions that people often ask when they witness faith in the face of a fatal prognosis. First, how to balance the facts of medical diagnosis against the truth and veracity of God's Word? This is a question I will answer later in this tale, at a point when I myself was in the firing line.

The other question that comes up is this: Why are some people healed whilst others are not? There are no clear answers to that, so I will not claim to be an authority on the subject. I can only speak from my understanding of the Bible and my own experience.

Cancer is a disease that often devastates lives without warning, and its impact can be unpredictable at best. Patients and their loved ones are almost held to ransom by the uncertainty and rollercoaster ride that the different stages of treatment can be. There are many other deadly diseases, but cancer in its various stages and guises makes us uncomfortable. This is because we are aware that family life as we know it will never be the same again. No-one can predict how cancer will change patients and loved ones alike.

My first reaction to a diagnosis of cancer is to cry out to God, reminding Him of the promises of His word.

Some might deem me a simple-minded person who needs a crutch. I have discovered that it really does not matter how another human being views my stance as long as I can live in victory as opposed to a prison of crippling fear. The way I see it, the true test of whether I take the Father at His word is how I handle situations that seem to contradict the wonderful promises I know are mine.

Now, the fact that I trust totally in God's Word does not change the fact that my human frailty will show forth. For as long as I can remember, whenever I am distressed or anxious, I get headaches that can become migraines and painful stomach upset. This means that I can be going back and forth to the toilet for hours.

When this happened after my sister's diagnosis, I figured that stronger painkillers would do the trick – even though I had already been prescribed medicine for irritable bowel syndrome. Off I went to my GP for stronger painkillers.

Nothing could have prepared me for his response.

8

Tough Call: Will I, or Will I Not?

'The hardest thing in life is to know which bridge to cross and which to burn.'

– David Russell

When I went to my GP, my request was very clear – I just wanted stronger painkillers. I figured that should not be complicated, and I could just get on with things. Looking back now, I can only thank God from the bottom of my heart that I was in enough pain to go for the consultation in the first place *and* that my GP did not take the easy option by giving me another prescription. After looking through my notes, he asked me if there had been any recent changes in my life or family situation. To say I was surprised was putting it mildly.

I told him about my sister's diagnosis. As my family and medical history were already well-documented, he said that I needed to take time off work for stress. I was gobsmacked. I had always prided myself on being a resilient woman. A survivor. I would not take time off.

But the doctor did not give me a choice; I had to stop going to work from the following day. He then stated that he would refer me to the Cancer Genetics Department so that I could be referred for early mammograms. As if the other bombshells were not enough, he then dropped the biggest of the lot: he told me to seriously consider having a prophylactic (risk-reducing) bilateral mastectomy.

I did not even have to think. I let him know, in no uncertain terms, what a dim view I took of his suggestion. I thought, *"Typical man."* Talking to me about getting rid of my breasts – which I must say I was very fond of. I had an abundance of what many women pay plastic surgeons to enhance. Now I was being 'advised' to consider getting rid of them to cut the risk of having breast cancer. Not a chance!

As far as I was concerned at the time, putting me on the list for early mammograms was all the precaution I needed. Having the dubious pleasure of a mammogram 15 years ahead of most women in the country was bad enough as far as I was concerned. In the UK, only 5% of all breast cancer cases are linked to genetic factors. This means that only a small proportion of women would re-quire breast screening before the age of 50.

I can only say that God's grace has been amazingly at work in my life because left to myself, I would have dis-missed much of the information as overkill. It is a credit to my GP (who I believe was divinely put on my path at just the right time) that he never gave up trying to get me to change my mind. Over the next two years, he brought it up at every appointment – talk about persistence. I was like a student who just turned a deaf ear to a never-ending lecture, thinking it was of no use because my mind was made up about my course of action.

My resolution at the time was grounded in what I considered my good knowledge of breast health given my two previous surgeries. I have always prided myself on dealing with issues head-on, *not* running away from uncomfortable subjects, no matter how I feel. My preliminary research on what the prophylactic surgeries involved made me determined to stand my ground. After all, why would I willingly put myself in a situation where I would be in hospital for at least a few days and be unable to look after Amy for weeks on end? At that point, the thought of having to ask anyone for help was one I did not even consider.

#

When I met the genetics counsellor a couple of months later, I found out that it was not standard procedure to offer mammograms to women under 35 due to the dense nature of younger breasts. My 35th birthday was still a couple of months away, which meant that if my file had been referred straightaway, it would have been returned as premature. The decision was then made to send my file after my birthday, ensuring that within a couple of months I got the appointment for my first mammogram.

I had no prior knowledge of any of the above information, and the counsellor did not have to go over and beyond the call of duty to assist me – but he did. Without a shadow of a doubt, this was amazing grace at work yet again. I have heard grace defined as "unmerited favour." There was *nothing* I could have done to have known, and continue to know, such favour wherever I turned. My heavenly Father, Creator of the ends of the earth, the One who knows the end even before the beginning, went ahead of me. He deserves my undying gratitude, worship, and adoration.

'And we know that **all things** *work together for good to those who love God, to those who are called according to His purpose.'*

— Romans 8:28 NKJV

I have emphasised the two words above to make a point that can get lost when things are going haywire and life does not make sense. If the verse had stated that only *some things* work for our good as God's children, it would have made for much uncertainty. After all, how would we know how things will turn out for us? Taking my Father at His word, I know that, regardless of what life throws at me, everything will work for my good ultimately. It does not mean I get to understand or comprehend it, but it means I have yet another basis for unwavering trust.

Nobody wants to be buffeted by stormy winds and gales on every side. We all prefer things to move along nicely without the hard bumps. The promise and assurance of the above verse though is that even the most difficult of seasons will ultimately turn out for our good. This does not mean that we fully understand when we are in the thick of things.

There was something else that the genetics counsellor did for me that proved to be one of the best gifts ever. This was the introduction to Maggie's Centres, an international charity that provides free practical, emotional and social support to people with cancer and their loved ones. This was a safe place where I could walk in to speak to professionals and volunteers who knew what the cancer journey is all about. Over the past six years, it has been a wonderful resource for me at various times.

#

Of all the things involved in breast screening, I have got to say that the mammogram is my least favourite part. Once the first one was over and done with, I breathed a sigh of relief that I did not have to think about it for another year.

How mistaken I was. A few weeks later, I received a letter from the test centre asking me to return for more testing as further checks were required. It was my right breast this time.

Father in heaven, again? I can honestly say that my initial response was to block things out for the first few hours until I could get into my room to pray. That is when I let rip. After about half an hour of ranting at the Father about the unfairness of my situation, I calmed down enough to be still and know that He is indeed God. In His enduring love, He does not despise my human frailty, for which I am immensely grateful.

This just reminds me of the way He dealt with Elijah in 1 Kings 19:4–18. Despite Elijah's great victory, threats from the wicked Queen Jezebel were enough to make him despondent. The Lord showed His love for the prophet by ministering to him with compassion. How much more will He extend His unfailing kindness to those of us who are recipients of grace through the atoning sacrifice of Christ?

Once the peace of God which surpasses all understanding took root, all efforts of the enemy to derail me were foiled. Now let me make myself very clear – problems did not disappear overnight. If anything, there was a bumpy ride ahead. Through it all, though, my hope was in my heavenly Father and Him alone.

On my return to the breast screening centre, I viewed the magnified images of my breast. There were tiny dots which, to my untrained eye, looked like specks of salt. They were breast calcifications, tiny flecks of calcium that may or may not indicate early stages of cancer. Biopsy samples were then taken for testing to determine one way or another.

Unfortunately, the samples were too small to get a conclusive result. It was decided that surgery was the only way to go. The radiologist had to insert what looked like a metal spring into me, acting under ultrasound guidance, so that the breast surgeon would know which parts to remove, given that the calcifications were not visible to the naked eye.

Every time I thought I was okay, that nothing new could faze me, that notion was knocked sideways. Prior to the procedure, I saw the machine that would be used. I took a photograph of the equipment because it all seemed so unreal.

Thank God for peace and a good sense of humour. Time and time again, this was my saving grace. Even during serious consultations, I try to find the humour – or at least the ridiculous. I do not always succeed, but I do give it a good try.

People can mistake my humour for denial, but nothing could be further from the truth. Before every single appointment, if I know what to expect, I do my best to read whatever information on the subject is available. If I do not know in advance, the 24–48 hours after the appointment is my research time. Thank God for the internet; a lot of information is at my fingertips.

Caution: information gathering should be done wisely and not to excess. I tend to visit and read up on the websites of governing health bodies, reputable charities, and centres of research excellence. Once I am in possession of the salient facts, I then hand it over to the Father and get into the Word to remind me of the promises that are mine.

I find this to be a fool proof plan every single time. Different things will work for different people, but I do not think ignorance is an option. Neither is being bound by fear because of information overload. Without the assurance of the Word, it would be difficult for me to remain sane.

#

I could go on and on about the invaluable prayers and practical support of my church family. At times when one's mental, physical, and spiritual reserves are low, it is so reassuring to know that there is constant prayer being offered on your behalf.

> 'The effective, fervent prayer of a righteous man avails much....'
>
> – James 5:16 NKJV

There have been so many times over the last few years when I have had people praying for me in different countries. This support was attributable to close friends who have friends and church connections in different countries. The reassurance that their messages of support kept me going through many dark times. This is yet another wonderful dimension of the Father's grace. How can I but magnify His name?

#

A couple of weeks after surgery, I was told that there was no malignancy – the result was atypical hyperplasia (in layman terms: precancerous cells). I could breathe a huge sigh of relief. Without the shadow of a doubt, I knew that this good news was a direct result of prayers. The Lord is still in the miracle-working business, and I will continue to testify to that every single day of my life.

My second mammogram nine months after that sur-gery came back all clear. I felt I could relax for another year. If that were the end of the story, I am sure you would agree that I had had more than enough of being prodded, and I should enjoy the next year hassle-free.

Wrong again.

9

Making the Tough Choice

'These things I have spoken to you that in Me you may have peace. In the world, you will have tribulation, but be of good cheer, I have overcome the world.'

— John 16:33 NKJV

I find that verse a bittersweet one: difficult to swallow, yet filled with the assurance of hope. I would not be human if I did not wish for a long sabbatical from this 'tribulation'. Anyone reading this can echo that sentiment.

So now what? About six months after the second mammogram, I felt another lump in my right breast. Not again! I could have gladly gone another 50 years without having to see a breast surgeon. Now – do not get me wrong – most of the ones I have had were brilliant. I was just plain tired of being poked.

The unease of dealing with breast changes and examinations is something I think only women can fully appreciate. No matter what size our breasts are, they are part of what makes us uniquely feminine. I think that is why the female cancers (breast, womb, uterine, and cervical) will shake a woman's concept of her femininity. This, of course, also feeds into self-image and ideas of what constitutes beauty.

Yes, as a child of God, I know that my sense of worth is not tied to my body parts, however lovely they are and however attached I am to them. But this does not mean I cannot love certain parts of my body. The way I see it, the natural bits are God's gifts to me, and at that time, I was pleased that I did not need plastic surgery to enhance or modify my body.

But with the discovery of yet another lump, the prospect of another round of testing, and possible surgery, I realised it was time to seek the Father's face about what my next step would be. I had to be honest with myself about why I had been resisting the idea of risk-reducing bilateral mastectomy.

If my refusal had to do with a clear instruction from the Father, then as His child, I could rest on that. Some readers may disagree with this, but I believe it all boils down to a personal relationship with God and how He speaks to us as individuals. Godly counsel has a place when it comes from trusted and seasoned believers who themselves are led by the unshakeable Word of God as well as the inner witness of the Holy Spirit. But it is in the intimacy of the secret place that we get to understand and know the Father better. There are no hard and fast rules when it comes to decisions like this.

Nowhere is it more important for me to do away with pretence as in the secret place. After considerable soul-searching, I realised that my rejection of what is, admittedly, a major and life-changing surgery was based on my vanity. For all my so-called piety, that was the truth.

Once I accepted that, it went without saying that vanity was a poor foundation on which to base a decision of such magnitude. I was then able to seek the counsel of the Holy Spirit on the matter. I concluded that I was to go ahead with the surgery. I had the Father's promise to be with me every step of the way.

If anyone were to ask me how I knew this was the right choice, the only response I could give is this: It is the same way that I know I am forgiven, saved, and Spirit-filled. It does not have to be any more complicated than that. As far as I was concerned, with the Father on my side, all would be well.

As difficult as making the decision was, I later realised that this was the easiest part. A bumpy ride awaited me.

#

With the decision made, I thought things would move fast so I would not have too much time to brood. Wrong again. For starters, my GP was away for a month, and I did not relish the idea of starting all over again with another doctor. Therefore, I had a whole month to reflect upon this decision I had made.

During the month of waiting, so many thoughts went through my head. I was praying that the test results on the lump would come back benign. I also tried without success to imagine what my body would look like after the surgery. In the waiting period, I made a choice to read up (as much as I could stomach) on bilateral mastectomy with immediate reconstruction.

Despite all that was going on in my head, I was incredibly at peace with the decision. I knew I had the assurance of the Father's presence with me every step of the way, and I committed everything into His hands.

This is an area in which I think our theology could do with some reworking. Just because the Father is in charge does not mean we will not be subject to the vagaries of our human nature. So often, we expect that because the Father is with us on the journey that should preclude tears and pain along the way. Nothing could be further from the truth.

The difference between a journey of hope and one filled with despair is God's boundless, outrageous grace – we know the reality and the truth of His infallible Word. This grace meant that, no matter what, I was surrounded by His love and support.

#

There were days when my head spun and hurt as I researched what the procedure would entail. The options for reconstruction were either to use a breast implant or my own tissue.

I have always believed in doing research and making sure that I avail myself of all the facts. Bearing that in mind, I decided that reconstruction using implants would not work for me. Implants have a limited shelf life, and I did not want to contemplate the idea of going through the procedure again in another 10–15 years. A major factor in this decision was my age. If I were 30–35 years older, there is no doubt that I would have considered implants. However, as a 37-year-old woman, it was imperative that I take a long-term view. Using my own tissue seemed the best way forward.

After looking at all the options, I chose the type of reconstruction surgery that would use tissue from my belly. This was one of the longest surgeries and had the lengthiest recovery period. So, not only was I making this drastic decision, but I was going one of the hardest routes possible.

At about this time, I realised that I needed a safe place to talk about some of the thoughts that were taking up residence in my head. The images I had seen online were – to put it mildly – unflattering. I nearly chickened out at this stage because I could not imagine someone sticking plasticine on my chest (I am just calling it as I saw it). All the things that I had said to other women about what constitutes beauty and how it is not just skin deep – they were now put to the test.

Once my mind was made up, I went to see the psychologist at Maggie's Centre as I had a lot to process mentally. In the counselling room, I found the space to express and explore the thoughts that were running through my mind no matter how ridiculous or outlandish they might be. I will talk about this in more detail after I describe my first appointment with the plastic surgeon. But I want to make one thing clear: women who are about to go through this procedure for the first time are often counselled to speak to a psychologist, and I think that is brilliant advice. It is a recognition and acknowledgement of what a huge step this is for any woman.

When I finally saw my GP, and told him that I was ready for the referral, the look of relief on his face is one I will not forget. His dedication to my health and well-being, as evidenced by his persistence, is something I now know to be a priceless gift.

Upon reading the referral letter from my GP, the first breast surgeon I saw took down my family and medical history. Then he gently asked me if I realised the implication of the decision I was making. Okay, I knew the man was doing his job, but I was already wondering how many more times I would have to parrot the same information repeatedly.

One issue that I had not expected to be broached was that of child-bearing. Was I planning to have any more children? Because if I was, then it was not advisable for me to go ahead with the procedure. Here comes the reality check. I had understood this in theory, but the reminder turned it from an abstract idea into something that was actually going to happen.

#

Waiting several months to see the plastic surgeon was agonising. For the better part of my life, I had always been the strong one in my family – the one who just sucked it up and got on with things. Over this period, it felt like my tear ducts were making up for lost time. There was a part of me that used to get (and sometimes still gets) cross when I cry unexpectedly. I expect my pep talks to myself to stem the tide of tears; a silly prospect, yet one I have not been able to dismiss entirely.

I suppose it is a fair question to ask why I cried so much. After all, I knew the peace of God which surpasses all understanding, and I had the support of friends and colleagues alike. The answer to this is rooted in what I had repressed for more than two decades – pain, grief, helplessness, disappointment, and fear. These were some of the feelings I had when I watched my mum get ill, gradually decline, and then pass away. At that time, there was no avenue or opportunity to deal with any of them. However, when I made the choice to get a bilateral mastectomy, there was no hiding these emotions.

Growing up the way I did, I told myself repeatedly that being tough was a necessary survival tool. I grew up with the false concept that crying is a sign of weakness to eschew at all costs. At times, I wished I could have one long crying jag, get it out of my system, and then know that bit was done and dusted. I can only attribute that wish to the part of me that wants to be in control and keep things from getting messy. Over the years, I have realised the error of my ways. Have I had a lot to learn!

Sometimes, crying is a huge relief and stops my tension headaches.

Considering that quite a few of my pre-surgery meltdowns took place at work, you would think that I must have had very understanding bosses. Otherwise, I would have ended up in big trouble. That has been one of the greatest blessings that the Father has bestowed upon me over the years. In times of crisis, I find myself surrounded by wonderful people who provide the support that I need there and then. The managers and colleagues that I had at the time were very supportive. This did me a world of good at the time.

However, this state of things did not remain so with change of managers and teams after subsequent surgeries. It is interesting to note that within the same organisation, my experience of being managed at work during difficult seasons varied from good to bad. Despite my experiences of others, in difficult times, my anchor is secure. That is what forms the basis of my gratitude.

#

After doing a fair amount of reading, I figured I was prepared for my first appointment with the plastic surgeon. There should not be any major surprises. I am sure by now you must be wondering where I get some of these funny ideas.

I love planning. I suppose it is a coping mechanism for me – sort out those things that are within my control and trust the Father with the rest. However, I do better when I commit everything into His hands and let Him take control because He knows the end from the beginning. He will always do a better job than I could ever do.

'Trust in the Lord with all your heart and lean not on your own understanding. In all your ways acknowledge Him and he shall direct your paths.'

– Proverbs 3: 5–6 NKJV

At my first consultation with the plastic surgeon, it was apparent that the Lord had gone ahead of me. Here was a doctor who did not patronise me or dismiss my concerns in any way whilst still getting across to me all the pertinent facts. When I could not get my head around some of the details, he even drew a rough sketch (amusingly, this took me back to my biology lessons in school, only this was real-life and very clear).

I think the concept of breast reconstruction using tissue from the belly is complicated for anyone who is not medically trained, and I was no exception. It sounded like a very elaborate medical procedure that you might see on television. From my preliminary research, I thought the surgery would take about 7–8 hours. I learned that the duration would be a minimum of 10 hours. Now, that was a surprise! As I got the explanation for what could possibly take so long, I was amazed that the surgery itself did not rattle me. I was more concerned about the aesthetic and cosmetic implications.

Was this shallow or vain of me? In this instance, not really. You see, I had a picture in my head of what breasts should look like, but what I was told I would live with for at least six months did not match up to that. Talking this through with a psychologist was a blessed relief. There were just too many things I could not share with loved ones so as not to cause them pain or make them uncomfortable. In counselling, I found space to be myself.

I received written information to take with me and was told to bring all my questions to the next consultation in another 6–8 weeks. When the surgeon stated that he would answer any question, I have got to be honest, I did not believe him. After all, brushing aside questions about finer details is what these clever medics do best – or so I thought.

Before the next consultation, a breast reconstruction awareness evening was organised by the plastic surgery department. It was designed to bring together women who had already undergone reconstruction and those awaiting surgery. I will forever be grateful to those women who freely shared their experiences. As it was a female-only event, some were quite candid about their scarring, healing process, and their reconstructed breasts. It was quite reassuring to discover that I was not the only one who felt tired and overwhelmed. One presentation showed colour pictures of what was underneath the top layer of skin in graphic detail. To someone who is not medically-trained, it was horrifying. The collective gasp from most of us in the audience spoke volumes.

When I went home that night after the event, it is difficult to explain what was going through my mind. Amy was sleeping over at her friends' house, so she could not see that anything was amiss. For that, I am very grateful. I desperately wanted to block out the images in my head and my sadness about what I had to face.

When I got to work the following morning, I could not hold it together. I went to the ladies' room to have a good cry. I was fortunate that a friend chose that moment to come in along with another colleague. I was then able to get things off my chest and get on with my day.

#

Eight days after the reconstruction awareness evening, Amy and I went on a much-needed holiday abroad. The whole way this trip came about – timing, provision, and so on – was yet another testament to the faithfulness and loving-kindness of the Father. We experienced such favour on our journey and had a brilliant time. For me, it was an opportunity to de-stress and count my blessings without getting weighed down thinking about what lay ahead for me in the coming months.

While abroad on this vacation, I had an unpleasant learning experience. I will share it as a cautionary tale for those who find themselves in similar situations. For most of our trip, we stayed with very good friends of mine. We however spent a couple of nights with another family who I had been acquainted with previously. These hosts offered us a warm welcome, for which I was grateful. During our conversation, however, I spoke about my decision regarding upcoming surgery. My hosts said that my decision was the wrong one and that if I trusted God, I would not go forward with surgery. They gave me a book of healing sermons by a prominent 20th-century preacher. Supposedly, this was meant to re-energise my faith.

They even suggested possible reasons for my predicament. Perhaps I had offended at God in some way, or I was not in right standing with God, or I was not fulfilling my God-given assignment, or maybe – just maybe – I had not asked forgiveness for conceiving my child out of wedlock 10 years before. As a guest, I could not disrespect my hosts, but at the same time, a so-called pastoral counsel that was based on a minute knowledge of my life and walk with God was bound to be flawed.

Praise be to the Father that I am getting to know Him for myself daily as well as His ways of speaking to me as an individual. Without knowing those truths deep in my heart, I would have been in big trouble, as you will discover later in this book.

*'If we confess our sins, He is faithful and just to forgive us our
sins and to cleanse us from all unrighteousness.'*
　　　　　– 1 John 1:9 NKJV

I know my heavenly Father does not keep score of
wrongs or mark my transgressions. If He did, Jesus Christ
died in vain, and I (along with millions of other Christians) would not be assured of salvation or eternal life. I
also would not be the recipient of the grace that is woven
into the fabric of my life.

Let me be clear: there will always be a place for wise
and godly counsel.

*'Where there is no counsel the people fall, but in the multitude
of counsellors there is safety.'*
　　　　　– Proverbs 11:14 NKJV

But any counsel that contradicts what I know of the
truth of God's Word is one I will not take on board. God
is not the author of confusion. He will not promise to be
with me and then change His mind five months later.

On matters of health and well-being especially, I think
it is imperative to proceed with caution when giving counsel. Unless you are walking in another person's shoes on a
daily basis, you cannot begin to comprehend the impact of
long-standing health issues. Neither can you understand
the courage it takes to go ahead with radical surgery or
treatment.

Thank God for His grace. As always, the Holy Spirit
reassured and encouraged me in the middle of it all. My
holiday was not marred by the experience at all. I just
learnt a few things about our interactions as believers.

\#

A week after our holiday, I had my second plastic surgery consultation. This was my last chance to ask every question I had and be very clear whether I still wanted to go ahead with the surgery or not. It was crunch time. No going back. As I knew the Father's leading and His all-encompassing peace, there was no doubt in my mind that this was the right decision for me.

At the second consultation, I got to grips with the finer details of the procedure (as well as a person with no medical training whatsoever could). This was when I discovered that I would be unable to perform basic domestic activities for up to six weeks.

I had always prided myself on running my life like a well-oiled machine. Having control of my daily schedule – things like getting Amy to school on time, pulling my weight at work to create a warm, inviting, and safe home – was important to me. I began to sense that maybe this surgery was going to have a bigger impact on my day-to-day life than I'd originally thought.

I was not deluded. I did comprehend how major the surgery that I had spent considerable time researching would be. But I'd always thought my inner strength and forbearance would stand me in good stead. This stance was sorely tested in the weeks leading up to the surgery.

#

In the couple of months between the second plastics consultation and the first surgery, I went through such a rollercoaster of emotions that I felt like I was spinning. Yes, there was a part of me that had made peace with my decision and all it would entail. But there was also a part of me that felt as if I were on the outside looking into someone else's life.

Like it or not, life goes on, and I got on with things as best I could. In that respect, making sure that Amy was not burdened with my internal struggles was a character test that I hope not to go through too often. There was time enough to prepare her for what was ahead. In the meantime, she could just be an everyday 9-year-old with no cares or worries. Getting through Christmas that year (2013) was a mixed bag, as far as I was concerned. Yes, I was mega grateful to spend time with Amy, and yet I knew that in the New Year, her world would change forever.

During this time of waiting and preparation, there were practical matters to attend to, like cooking in bulk to stock my freezers so that I did not have to worry about food for at least the first six weeks after surgery. It goes without saying that such a season is filled with learning curves that should make us better people at the end of it. Notice my use of the word *should*, as that will be the expectation, but it is not always the case. Often, we are so busy complaining or just being grumpy that the lessons we are supposed to learn go right over our heads.

Having experienced first-hand the confusion and devastation caused by the secrecy surrounding my mother's diagnosis, I was determined that Amy would not go through the same. Once I got the date for the surgery, I went through intense mental struggle on when and how to prepare Amy for what was about to happen.

Just over a month before the scheduled surgery date, I spoke to Amy's headteacher about the possibility of support for Amy through the process. We then both agreed to tell her a couple of weeks before the surgery date. Some people might wonder why I made the decision to include Amy's headteacher as opposed to speaking to her in private.

I figured that with the amount of time she spent in school, I will have to notify them anyway as practical arrangements had to be changed for more than half a term and I also did not want to have the conversation twice. This is one of those situations where as a parent I made the best decision I could given how well I know my child. As a single parent, the buck stops with me so I had to put my pride aside to ensure that Amy had the best support possible.

Now that is one meeting that I never want to go through again. In her headteacher's office, I explained as simply as I could what the surgery was about and why I was going through with it. Amy, being the intelligent child that she is, was particularly baffled by my choice of such a radical procedure when there was nothing wrong with me. I then had to give her insight into my family history of breast cancer and why prevention was a better option for me. She started crying and climbed into my lap, a little girl who needed her mother's comfort. By this time, I was crying as well because it tore me apart to see her distressed. Eventually, she calmed down, and after some persuasion left to attend her classes.

I had to do some serious soul-searching before I decided to tell Amy, but that is one decision I would not change. Like it or not, my surgery would have a major impact on her anyway. I would be in hospital for at least a week, and she would have to stay with friends for the duration. There was also the reality of the immediate aftermath of surgery once I got home. Through it all, the amazing grace of God was our succour. I raised Amy on the importance of prayer, so she knew we could both anchor ourselves to God knowing He would carry us through.

As surgery date approached, I decided that some relaxation time was necessary for Amy and me. So, three days before surgery, I took her on a weekend break out of town. This was an opportunity for me to focus on life and love instead of the difficulties ahead. We got our hair done, ate too much, stayed up late, and just had lots of fun. I was so glad for the opportunity to do that; at the time, I thought it would be about three months before we could go away again.

The journey back home was, inevitably, a more sombre experience, as I would be admitted into hospital that same night. However, our spirits were not dampened because we had enjoyed such a fab time away. Within an hour of returning home, my friend came to pick both of us up. She dropped me off at hospital first. My friend and Amy came into the ward with me, dropped my things, went to get chocolates from the hospital café, and then I sent Amy off with a big kiss and a hug. I was assured that she would be well-looked after.

The Father was true to His Word: everything worked out well. The support of a few friends through this whole journey has amazed and humbled me in equal measure. To have such a support network in Wales where I have no relatives or close family members is only possible through divine providence, for which I am eternally grateful.

As I settled into my hospital bed for the night, the Word that dropped into my spirit was this:

> *'You will keep in perfect peace all who trust in You, all whose thoughts are fixed on You! Trust in the Lord always, for the Lord God is the eternal Rock.'*
>
> *– Isaiah 26:3–4 NLT*

The peace that surrounded me was so beautiful. I just basked in it. I can honestly say that I did not have any worry or anxiety about the surgery, such was the assurance that I was held in the Father's embrace. This was also the point at which I most appreciated all the people praying for me around the world. Most of these people I will probably not meet on this side of Heaven, yet they gave up their time to pray for me. Words cannot express my gratitude that I am so richly blessed. The messages and phone calls of encouragement were simply priceless and made such a positive difference, both before and after surgery.

Before I went to sleep, I was given the information that I needed, had some blood taken for tests, and got the all-important name badge. Having been told I could not eat or drink past midnight, I decided to eat as many snacks as I could get away with before I went to sleep. The human mind is very funny, I think. When you are told you cannot eat, it is interesting how your craving for all sorts of food increases until you shut it down through self-discipline and determination.

That first night, I had a good night's sleep. I must admit, I took it for granted. I would soon find out that sleep is not a given when one is an inpatient.

Part III

Wrecking Ball

10 | The Big Surgery

> 'In times of adversity and change, we really discover
> who we are and what we are made of.'
>
> – *Howard Shultz*

On the day of the surgery, I woke up at my usual time
of 6 a.m., still with the sense of peace surrounding and
permeating my whole being. I made sure I had my shower
before any of the surgeons made an appearance. I would
not get to have another shower for eight days, just before
discharge from hospital.

It is interesting how one minute the ward is quiet, and
the next minute it is bustling with activity as the night
nurses hand over to the day nurses and the breakfast trol-
ley is wheeled in.

I was told to change into the hospital gown. I knew
in my head that vanity had no place here. But whilst I
appreciate that hospital gowns are made a certain way to
allow easy access to parts of the body, I still feel keenly the
loss of dignity that comes with wearing one. Needs must,

you chin up and await whatever medical examination is deemed necessary as part of your treatment.

One of the surgeons who had seen me the night before and got me to sign the consent forms came to check that I was ready for what was to come. About half an hour later, the consultant plastic surgeon came with his black marker. He explained to me that he had to draw on the parts where incisions would be made.

I felt I had to detach myself a little bit from what was happening. I just found it surreal. I cannot speak for anyone else, but I think it was at that point that I started feeling like a lab rat. This feeling would persist months down the line in my reconstruction journey.

Less than an hour after the markings were made, one of the lovely nurses on the ward walked me to the operation theatre. I am so glad that I had such a fabulous care team and that I had established a rapport with them in such a short space of time.

On getting to the theatre, I was met by the anaesthetists. There were three of them to start with; I am not sure how many stayed the course. The lead anaesthetist had previously come to introduce herself and ask me some questions a couple of hours before, so at least there was a familiar face.

The moment of truth had now arrived.

How do I even begin to put into words this moment that I had been preparing for over the previous eight months? I just took a deep breath and thought about how fortunate I was to be enveloped in such peace that I was not fazed by what lay ahead.

Of course, there was the uncomfortable part where the mask is put on. For just a couple of seconds, you feel like you cannot breathe, and then it is gone. It is almost like you imagined it. By this time, the anaesthetists were speaking to me, trying to get me to relax. Truth be told, it worked. I am probably just a lightweight, because they started counting from number one, and I cannot remember anything after number five.

#

When I came to, my first words were 'that was quick'. The human brain is a fascinating organ. I had no recollection of anything between the moment I was knocked out and when I came to with the illusion that it was just a short interval. After those first few words, I vaguely remember being wheeled to the monitoring unit before sleeping until the following morning.

When I finally woke up the day after surgery, I saw dressings covering the top part of my body. It looked like a patchwork quilt. As I would discover later, this was the beginning of my journey towards the 'new normal'. My first waking thought was to wonder whether the surgery had taken place or if I had imagined it all. On trying to move, I felt the discomfort of the IV line (through which morphine was administered) as well as four drains (two on either side).

That was when reality hit. The surgery had taken place, and my body as a woman would never be the same again. When that sense of inevitability hits you, it almost takes your breath away. One of the big lessons I have learnt is that if you ever hit a big storm of any kind, think about it – yes – cry if you need to, but do not dwell on it to the point of despair. Despair causes great men and women to crumble in the face of a new normal.

I had a couple of wires attached to aid in the monitoring that would continue for the next few days. This monitoring was to ensure that the transferred tissue stayed alive. The first 48–72 hours after surgery were the most crucial. Any tissue that survived past that timeframe was then viable in the future. Tissue death (or necrosis) is one of the major complications that the medical team had to be on the alert for. The primary way to detect tissue without a blood supply is a change in skin colour. My amazing black skin made me a special case – hence the wires.

To a layperson, all these processes and procedures can be fascinating and frustrating in equal measure. Thank God for medicine and those who have dedicated their lives to its study and practice. Most importantly, praise our heavenly Father God for making us so wonderfully. Of a certainty, we are the pinnacle of His creation. I suppose I now appreciate this better since my body parts have been 'reconfigured'.

#

Anyone who has spent more than one night in hospital will attest to the dragging of the days and the feeling of life passing by whilst you are stuck in your hospital bed. It is vital to find something to occupy one's time. Being the resourceful woman that I am, I discovered prior to admission to hospital that there was free Wi-Fi. However, did we survive before the advent of the internet? By listening to uplifting music on my laptop and YouTube, I could occupy myself during the very long nights when sleep came only in snatches of a couple of hours at best.

Visits from friends from far and near became the highlights of my days. During my hospital stay, a visit from Amy during a school day touched me deeply. Her headteacher had asked me beforehand if I wanted a visit, and she went out of her way to bring Amy so that she was reassured soon after the surgery.

This was one of the many instances when the entire staff of Amy's school rallied round and gave us support that went over and beyond the call of duty. You may wonder how to get such support. One answer is to open up to reasonable people around you. At the very centre of each one of us is the nature to help one another irrespective of colour, race, creed, etc. This core human nature, which God graciously placed in us, may be warped or twisted by sin, but it often shines through when it is most needed.

I appreciate that we often want to keep painful experiences in our lives private. This is especially true when these experiences are of a sensitive nature. My personal view, though, is that we weather storms better if we do it in community. No matter how well-resourced we are within our family units, there are times when the support of strangers is required. In the case of those with school-age children, it is impossible to watch them round the clock whilst we are tending to other needs. The school's support allowed Amy to have the semblance of normality and a safe place to talk whenever she needed to.

Between the constant monitoring and the hustle and bustle of activity, sleep in hospital becomes a luxury. When one of your roommates happens to be a very distressed patient who cries all night, your exhaustion levels rise, and your patience wears thin. I must admit that at some point I asked one of the nurses why the patient could not be moved or given something to knock her out. God forgive me, my thoughts were not charitable at all. I thank Him for His grace and mercy when I least deserve it.

#

I remember telling one of the nurses that I was surprised that I hardly felt any pain. She let me know that it was the morphine drip that kept the pain at bay and that once it was removed, I would appreciate that fact. Note to self: When medical professionals give you advice about physical limitations after medical procedures, do not dismiss or discount what they say. Time and time again, I have done just that because I think I am made of sterner stuff. When will I learn?

On the day after surgery, one of the nurses came to assist me in changing my clothes, and she discovered a wound on my lower back that no-one had known about. As it was late in the day, the nurses did their best to dress the wound and promised to inform my surgeons when they came on their morning rounds.

The following morning (48 hours after surgery), when my plastic surgeon came and saw the wound, to say he was not amused is an understatement. He grilled the nurses on duty, wanting to know what they had done to me. He then told them to order a specialist dressing and told them sternly to keep an eye on the wound. Over the course of that day, all the other surgeons on the team came to check up on me as they were baffled about the wound. The lead anaesthetist came to see me the next morning and assured me that she had checked me over before I was transferred to the ward.

I told one of the nurses to take a picture of it with my phone, as I could not see it otherwise. I then realised why my surgeons were so concerned. It looked like a hot iron had burnt through the skin. Ironically, this wound was the last one to heal, over a month later.

To date, no-one knows for sure what happened. I was not in bed long enough to develop bed sores. The hypothesis was that my body had a rare reaction to some chemical that had been used on the surface that I was placed upon during surgery. That was my hospital mystery with all its attendant drama. There was never a boring moment.

Whilst all the commotion over my back was going on, I felt wiped out. Given what my body had just been through, I thought this was natural and that I should just get on with it. One of the regular blood tests then revealed that my haemoglobin level was seriously low. On checking the result, one of my surgeons came to ask why I had not complained earlier. I told him that I'd thought this was a normal side effect of the surgery. I was then given three pints of blood in quick succession, and the blood test was repeated afterwards.

During this journey, I have constantly sought to strike the right balance between asking for help and being a shrew who does not stop talking about her physical symptoms.

I know that my default mode is to keep quiet altogether, telling myself to suck it up and just get on with it. I am still learning how to get across the fact that I am not as super-healthy as people presume I am by how I look (the wonders of makeup) whilst not becoming a burden or a drain on those around me. I know I have a lot to learn about that, as time and time again loved ones tell me to open up more when I am hurting. As I am the type who wants to look after everyone around me, I need reminders to properly look after myself and ask for help when I need it. What can I say? I am work in progress just like everyone else.

People have asked me this time and time again: 'Did you ever say, "Why me"?' I suppose if ever there was a time to ask that question during my rollercoaster journey, this should have been it. I can honestly say that I never once asked that question. You see, I realised a few years ago that this kind of thought could easily open the door to lasting despair and dejectedness.

Yes, I have asked for the pain to be over quickly and for everything to be back to normal. I would not be human if I did not want a quick reprieve from all that my body has been subjected to. But I quickly discovered that my normal had changed forever. This is the new normal, a journey that I have never been on before and one that can only be navigated by grace. That amazing grace has undergirded me in unbelievable ways for which I am so grateful.

#

I only spent eight days in hospital on this stint, but it felt like longer. This was probably because of the drastic change in my body between admission and discharge. Never again will I take any part of my body for granted. As wonderful as my entire medical team was, I had a massive smile on my face when my plastic surgeon came to discharge me. No-one likes hospital, and I suppose my delight at being told I could leave is mirrored by millions of people who for one reason or another had to be hospital inpatients.

Towards the end of my hospital stay after the big surgery, I had the idea to write a hospital diary (you can read these entries in Appendix 1). It was nothing extensive, by any means, just a way to catalogue my thoughts at the time.

As a patient, whether in a medical facility or your home, you end up with a lot of time on your hands during and after treatment. This also applies to other kinds of trauma whether you are directly or indirectly affected. The human mind is such a powerful thing, and it is important to guard your thoughts as much as you possibly can in difficult times. One of the tools that I have found to be most useful is journaling. In different seasons of life, it has helped me stay sane when I would have sunk into a pit of despair. I encourage you to give it a shot. There are no rules; just do it your way.

11

Big Surgery Aftermath

'Recovery is a process. It takes time. It takes patience. It takes friends.'

— Unknown

There is something about sleeping over in hospital that makes you seem far removed from the outside world. On the one hand, you lose a sense of time (if your stay is a long one), which can make you feel left out and caged. On the other, you accept with equanimity the strangeness of being looked after – no matter how independent you otherwise might be.

The reality that life as I knew it would never be the same again did not sink in until after I had left hospital. Up until the moment when I finally left the plastics ward, the quality of care that I received from the staff was brilliant. As my mobility was still limited, one of the nurses put on her Wellington boots and came into the bathroom to give me a refreshing shower (my first in a week). I would not have another shower for the next two weeks. I had my dressings changed, and then I had friends from church come to pick me up. One person carried my suit-case, and another pushed me in the wheelchair, as I could not walk the distance from the ward to the car park.

I remember been told prior to surgery by nurses and my plastic surgeon that I would not be able to do house-work for at least six weeks. To be honest, I did not think it would be that bad. I figured that as a strong black woman, I was made of sterner stuff. I soon realised I was seriously mistaken.

On leaving hospital, I went to Shalom4, a short-stay respite centre for ladies. The owner, Sue (whom I fondly call my Welsh mother), offered to look after me there until my close friend from London arrived to take over. What was special was that she cared for me as only a mother could – with endless patience and practical wis-dom that sure made a difference!

In the whole of the week in hospital, I could not open my bowels no matter what medicine I was given. By the 9th day, I was so uncomfortable my belly felt like it would explode. What the medicines did not achieve was sorted out by eating fresh prunes with dried raisins, currants, and sultanas. In less than 24 hours, I could go! What pain, and what relief afterwards! Prunes and mixed fruit became a daily part of my diet for the next four weeks.

This four weeks coincided with the length of time I had to keep wearing the DVT (compression) socks, which were difficult to put on. As I could not deal with most of my personal care needs now, they had to be put on for me. For the final two weeks, my 9-year-old daughter had to do the honours. Apart from nurses who have done it many times before, everyone agrees that for an adult it puts a strain on your wrist. For a child, it was even worse, but not once did Amy complain or quibble.

#

Three days after discharge from hospital, the wound on my back started itching, and I wondered if my friend Sue could change the dressing for me. She looked and discovered that it was oozing – yikes. I called the ward for help and was told that if I could get someone to bring me to the hospital, the dressing would be changed. In a place like Swansea, assumptions are made about transportation and support that do not always hold true. Not everyone has a partner/parent/grandparent/cousin etc. who drives and can whisk them to hospital at a moment's notice.

I was therefore told to contact my GP who made a referral to the district nurses. The following day, the first district nurse showed up at Shalom4. When she saw the number of dressings I had, she told me that the ward nurses who discharged me should have made a referral, which they had not. Oh well, never mind. She sorted out my back first and then proceeded to the front of my body. She initially thought I had silicone implants so there was no reason I should have had dressings anywhere else. I will never forget her shock when I told her exactly what I had done. Over the next 10–15 minutes whilst she attended to me, she expressed how impressed she was with the plastic work. She was particularly impressed with the 'needlework' on the lower part of my abdomen. She told me to commend my plastic surgeon for a job well-done.

#

One of my oldest friends came from London to look after me for two weeks. She was a godsend. I would have been grateful under any set of circumstances, but since she had lots of her own work to do (which she had to bring with her and do whilst looking after me) – she has my heartfelt gratitude. That is a sacrifice you do not ever forget.

Nothing fazed her. Her compassion, kindness, and desire to see me get well was commendable. She did not shy from any unpleasant task. Whenever I see or eat a prune, I always remember her and smile. She ensured that I did the exercises required to restore mobility in my arms when, for the most part, I did not want to. Very good friends are rare; they make you laugh when you feel like crying, but they also tell you the truth in love when you least want to hear it. Thank God for them.

As friends of long standing, we "got" each other, especially when it came to our peculiar sense of humour. Whether keeping up an ongoing commentary when watching a chick flick or having a serious debate, we had such a fabulous time together that I did not slide into self-pity throughout her stay. Despite the circumstances, we had such a laugh, and the time together flew. For those couple of weeks, Amy was spared the task of my personal care, and before my friend left, she ensured that Amy understood the tasks she had to perform for me.

The week after that, another friend from out of town came with her young daughter to stay for a few days. Amy enjoyed their company so much; she was sad when they left. My friend brought and cooked my favourite foods, cleaned my house from top to bottom, and sorted my hair, which was a mess at the time.

I will never get tired of saying that throughout this journey, the Father has been so gracious to me by putting people around me for support at just the right time. The support and prayers of my church family have been essential all the way through. Whether ensuring that Amy got to church or giving me lifts to and from my hospital appointments, their actions were just another expression of the Father's amazing love for us.

I also must say that I am immensely grateful for the favour bestowed upon me that ensured I got paid for the duration of the time that I was off work. My manager and colleagues at that time gave me incredible support. I was kept supplied with flowers, chocolates, and pampering gifts while I stayed at home after the big surgery.

My original plan was that I would be off work for no more than three months. What I did not bargain for was that this would stretch into five months when a spanner was thrown in the works.

12 | Now What? Wrecking Ball in My Lap

'With this diagnosis, I had choices to make: fight or flight; sink or swim. As far as I was concerned, my choice was to fight and swim. I will not be me if I chose differently.'

— *Bamidele Adenipekun*

This journey was supposed to be mainly about plastic surgery, and all my mental preparation was geared towards that. As the mastectomy itself was preventative, I figured I was doing everything I could to keep cancer at bay.

During the mastectomy part of the big surgery, the breast tissues were sent for analysis as a matter of routine, unbeknownst to me. As I was only a plastics patient, the results were automatically sent to my plastic surgeon. That is when he realised that things had got complicated.

The first I knew about any test was when I got a phone call from one of the breast care nurses asking me to come in for the results of the biopsy on the removed breast tissue. As far as I was concerned, this was just a formality, so

I asked for the result on the phone. This was four weeks after my first reconstruction surgery. The nurse stated that she could not give me the information over the phone. I had to go to the breast clinic in person. She told me that I could be seen in a matter of days.

When I asked which breast surgeon I was supposed to see, she told me it was the same one who had done my mastectomy. I flat-out refused, as I had decided not to see him again after an unpleasant experience with him prior to the mastectomy. I had an appointment with him prior to the mastectomy where I expected him to briefly explain his part of the surgery to me. After all, that part will last about an hour and a half. He made comments that made me feel belittled and a burden. I then decided then that I would never see him again at the clinic.

I was so emphatic in my refusal that I was prepared to travel out of town to see another surgeon if need be. I was then told that I could see the consultant when she returned from leave in a fortnight. I gladly agreed to that. I was still of the opinion that they had probably just found some precancerous cells as they had two years before. I put the matter out of my mind.

#

I can still remember the sequence of events so clearly. A good friend from church came to pick me up from home. As it was a lovely spring day (11 March 2014), we decided to have a pub lunch first, so we had a good time. As usual, I took my painkillers before the worst of the pain kicked in.

On getting to the clinic, we found a long wait ahead of us. I was so relaxed; I just wanted to get the formality out of the way. I was already thinking that I would not have to visit the breast clinic again. When my name was called, my friend asked if I wanted her to come in with me or not. I told her to come in as there was nothing to this appointment.

Entering the room, I again noticed what I had two years previously. It is the nicest patient room, with a lovely painting on the wall, comfortable sofas, flowers on the table, and of course, a box of tissues. The irony never escapes me that this lovely room is also the place where many women are given the news that will change their lives forever.

We were ushered into the pretty room by the breast care nurse who was soon followed by the consultant breast surgeon. I had only heard of this woman by name, but all the patients spoke of her very fondly. I was glad that I had waited to see her.

As soon as everyone was settled, she said that my plastic surgeon had dropped some unexpected results in her lap. At the time, I was seriously tempted to roll my eyes and just say 'out with it already'. She told me that normally her team would have had time to prepare me for the results, give me information and support, the whole nine yards…. I am not sure if my impatience showed; I would not be surprised if it did.

The bottom line was that in the right breast there was a fibroadenoma (non-cancer tumour). I had experienced this previously and knew there was nothing to it. In the left breast, however, micropapillary type invasive ductal carcinoma (DCIS), also known as stage 1 breast cancer, was found. (I would later find out from my personal research that this is an aggressive form of breast cancer with a 75% to 100% chance of spreading into the lymph nodes). The positive part was that it had been discovered at the earliest stage possible.

As soon as I heard 'DCIS', I knew what she meant. I felt like I had just been hit by a high-impact vehicle, such was my profound shock. It was surreal. I knew that the other three people in the room – my friend, the surgeon, and the nurse – were waiting for my reaction.

I felt as though I had two choices, with only one possible response: fight or flight. Those two words ran on a continuous loop in my head for the rest of that day. I remember thinking that flight was not a viable option, as I could not escape from what was going on there and then. Believe me, I would have done a runner if I could. That only left me with the option to fight. I think that decision, made within five minutes of receiving the diagnosis, helped me immensely in the weeks and months to follow.

Everyone was quiet in the room whilst this was going on in my head. Once my choice was made, I spoke up to say that I would choose to look at my glass as half full rather than half empty. This was a crucial decision for me to make, as I would discover later when my mettle was tested time and time again.

I remember wondering out loud what was going to happen to my 'new beauties' (as I referred to my reconstructed breasts). After all, I had undergone a 12-hour surgery to get them, and my recovery was still ongoing. Everyone in the room laughed. A woman had to have her priorities, surely! I was relieved that they would not be tampered with.

There was no doubt that I was incredibly fortunate and blessed that the cancer had been detected. Without the mastectomy, it would not have been found for who knows how long. The left breast was supposedly the one without issues; the mammogram in October 2012 had come back clear. Thank God that I was not going about my business with cancer lurking inside, unbeknownst to me!

I then had to go into another room so that a fine needle biopsy of my left lymph node could be taken. Fortunately, I had taken painkillers at lunch before the appointment. Even then, the process was uncomfortable. Once the sample was taken, I was told to come back for my results the following week.

Before I left, my surgeon said she understood why I wanted to keep my 'beauties', as my plastic surgeon had done a brilliant job so far. I never take these comments for granted, I have to say. This is because, even if I hadn't seen pictures online of women who have had reconstruction and those who have not, I can still vividly remember what my mother's body looked like after her mastectomy in Nigeria 24 years ago. I know I am blessed.

#

When I told Amy about the breast cancer diagnosis, her first question showed a child's ability to cut to the chase. She wanted to be sure that cancer was not an illness she had to worry about for herself. My ability to reassure her was solely based on my faith that God is faithful and will keep her healthy.

However, the fact that I am grounded in my faith does not mean that I will not teach her about breast awareness at the appropriate time. I will advise her about genetic testing and get her up to speed with current information at the time she requires it.

This is one of those uncomfortable discussions we would like to avoid in church circles. My stance will always be that having unshakeable faith *does not* equal ignorance. It means that, even in the abundance of scientific and medical facts, I choose to trust God's Word above all else, knowing that there is *nothing* too difficult for Him. I also have a fundamental understanding that He is sovereign, so that means that the answers to my prayers might not materialise in the precise manner and time that I think they should.

13 The Cancer Patient's Journey

'First thing about being a patient – you have to learn patience.'

– *Oliver Sacks*

A week later, when I went for the results of the fine needle biopsy of the lymph node, I was told that even though it came back clear, the only way to check whether the cancer had spread or not was to take a representative sample of lymph nodes under general anaesthetic. In fact, whilst I was waiting to see the surgeon, an appointment had already been made for me to have the 45-minute surgery in six days.

Hold on a minute! This was going a bit too fast! I had barely got my head round the diagnosis. I asked for an extra week to prepare. I knew I had to make childcare arrangements and prepare mentally for that surgery.

At this appointment, I made a particularly significant decision in my post-cancer-diagnosis journey. My breast surgeon was of the opinion that because I was so young when I was diagnosed (37), chemotherapy would be my best treatment option before I commenced the oral drugs suited to my age and type of breast cancer. One statistical tool that doctors use after a cancer diagnosis is referred to as the Predict Tool here in the UK. Once the histopathology (laboratory results of cancer) is entered, it gives a guide of expected prognosis. According to the Predict Tool that day, I had a 90% chance of living more than 10 years if I took chemotherapy. That chance dwindled significantly if I did not have chemotherapy.

Sitting in that consulting room in 2014, I told my surgeon emphatically that I did not want chemotherapy. I was prepared to consider radiotherapy or any other form of cancer treatment as long as chemotherapy was off the table.

I will put a disclaimer right here. This is *not* the kind of advice I will ever give to anyone else facing cancer treatment. I am *not* dismissing the decades of advances in chemotherapy and the positive impact it has had on millions of cancer patients' lives. All I can say is that in my case at that point in time, I knew that chemotherapy *was not* the option for me.

As a child of God, I know that He deals with us as individuals and that He speaks to us in different ways. The instructions and guidance given to one person are different for another. Our physiologies and anatomies are not the same; what someone can tolerate might destabilise another's body.

The decision against chemotherapy was one I was resolute about, and I was unwavering in my stance. Even though I could tell that my breast surgeon had my best interests at heart, my mind was made up. Having read this far in this book, you are probably wondering how I could have willingly undergone a 12-hour surgery, and yet I dug my heels in when it came to chemotherapy, a more common treatment path. I could not have articulated my reasons beyond what I felt was divine guidance. This is a side of my faith walk that most people struggle with.

When my surgeon realised I would not budge, the next phase was to wait until the surgery to remove the sample lymph nodes, get the results of that test, and then discuss my case with the multi-disciplinary team that included the oncologists.

#

After that consultation, I remember getting home and sending an update email to a select group of loved ones who would hold me up in prayer and boost my faith along the way. I prayed fervently that, when the lymph nodes were tested, there would be no metastasis and the chemo-therapy option would be taken off the table.

Thank God, that prayer was answered; the lymph nodes came back all clear. I was also given the news that the oncologist gave me a chemo-free pass. I suppose the question is this: If my lymph nodes were not clear, would my stance have changed? Probably not. My conviction was too strong for me to dismiss. The Lord was so gracious and kind to keep things clear for me so that I could stick to a decision that I felt was in obedience to His leading. I was prescribed one of the most common drugs used to treat breast cancer – Tamoxifen. I was supposed to take it for ten years. Even though the lymph nodes were clear, medication was required to prevent any reoccurrence. The normal duration is five years but I was told that due to my family history, the longer duration will ensure that there wouldn't be a secondary diagnosis.

#

Each person's journey as a cancer patient within the hospital system is different. I have been blessed to have a mostly positive experience due to the dedication of staff who give their best in their calling as healthcare providers. But occasionally, a small minority can make the patient experience memorable for all the wrong reasons. One of these experiences took place the day I had the lymph node removal. I can only put this down to negligence on the part of the nurses who discharged me that day.

Before the surgery, the pharmacists came to ask if I had brought any medication from home. Good patient that I was, I told them I had, even though I was reluctant to. My drugs were taken from me and locked up in the patient cabinet next to my bed. These drugs were the painkillers that had been prescribed to me ever since the big surgery, as I had been in considerable pain for weeks on end. Whilst in theatre, I was given morphine for pain relief, so I did not need that as soon as I got to the ward. The surgeon had told me that if I was able to eat and drink four hours after the surgery, I could go home if I had another adult staying with me overnight. Once I was given the okay, I called my friend who came to pick me up.

When my friend was getting my things together, my brain was just blank. I knew there was something I meant to ask for, but for the life of me, I could not remember what it was. I went to the nurse's station to ask if there was anything they were supposed to give me, but they replied in the negative. I was already too groggy and fuzzy-headed, so I left with my friend. I got home at 8.00pm, and my friend settled me into bed and waited until another friend who was spending the night came with Amy.

By about 9.00pm, my pain levels were nearly unbearable. Only then did I remember that I took all my drugs with me to hospital and they were not returned to me. I called the nurses at the hospital to tell them, and they said that unless I could get someone to drive to the hospital (about 30–40 minutes away), there was nothing they could do. It was a weeknight, and my friend who brought me from hospital had already gone back to her house which was an hour's drive away. My other friend who spent the night could not leave me alone with Amy so I was stuck. I took what painkillers I had, which barely took the edge off, and I had a very uncomfortable night.

In the morning, I called the ward nurses for a couple of hours and tried to get them to contact my GP's surgery for a new prescription. The drugs that were held at the hospital had only been prescribed a couple of days before, and it was a considerable amount. Not only were the nurses unhelpful, but they also insinuated that it was my own fault for being in a hurry to get home after surgery. What planet were these people on? I had spent eleven-and-a-half hours in the hospital – practically the whole day – and the surgeon okayed me to go home.

The pain and the stress finally got the better of me. I just cried. My friend took over the calls; I just could not do anymore. Finally, 19 hours after hospital discharge, I got a new prescription from my GP.

The unfortunate by-product of that incident is that I will never again hand over my medication to hospital staff. In fact, I will not take it into hospital with me, contrary to what hospital admission letters request. This means that medication which could have gone to someone else in hospital is then given to me and other patients who have learnt the same painful lesson.

No-one should ever have to go through that kind of experience, and if the nurses had followed proper procedures, that unfortunate incident would have been avoided. Whether patients are in hospital for a few hours or weeks, they still deserve to be treated fairly and humanely. Actions that contradict that shame the majority of nurses in the NHS who are hardworking, going over and beyond the call of duty to give excellent care to patients.

#

There was bound to be a difference between caring for a cancer patient and being one myself. At no time was this more glaring than in the immediate aftermath of my lymph node removal.

I sure underestimated the potential impact of a 45-minute surgery. I thought it would be a glitch on the screen – here one moment and gone the next. This was probably the rudest awakening for me in terms of treatment.

For starters, I had a build-up of lymphatic liquid under my armpit which required weekly drainage for a month after surgery. The pain from this was not funny at all, and I had to keep a cushion under my armpit until the nurse drained it. I also had residual nerve damage in my left arm. There's still a weakness in my left arm extending to the wrist. This means that I sometimes drop things, so I have to be careful to let my right arm do most of the work. The swelling in the upper part of my arm became an intermittent issue resulting in my having to wear a lymphoedema arm sleeve three years' post-diagnosis.

Part IV

New Normal

Introduction

'When the tidal wave of trauma hits, your narrative is forever changed.'

— Bamidele Adenipekun

I define a new normal as the change in perspective, outlook, and day-to-day living that the trauma of serious illness, injury, or bereavement brings.

There are two crucial factors in the new normal journey: coping mechanisms and resilience. When the trauma of serious illness, injury, or bereavement comes crashing into our lives, our default coping mechanisms are based upon the inner strength we already possess.

A lot depends on one's age and maturity when the trauma happens. An event may be so shattering to one person's psyche and emotions that it triggers deeper emotional, psychological, or mental issues, but the same event will not be nearly so devastating for someone else. No matter how strong or old one is, the impact of trauma cannot be over-emphasised, not just to the individuals concerned but also to their nearest and dearest.

My early exposure to the trauma of illness and bereavement within a hostile environment was a double-edged sword. On the one hand, it meant that I had to learn how to hone my coping strategies in stormy seasons. On the other hand, it meant that I was incredibly hard on myself, often not asking for help until I was nearly at the breaking point.

As I am a Christian and a woman of Black African ethnicity, the issue of seeking professional psychological support is an uncomfortable one at best and a contentious one at worst. I have had to climb a steep learning curve with the support of friends and good counsellors. Whilst a lot is changing within the Christian community, there is still a long way to go before it is widely accepted that counselling is a crucial part of the healing process.

The best time to build effective storm defences is before a storm, *not* during the storm. In a literal sense, the fierceness of winds and rain in a storm often make it difficult to see the way ahead, and with debris flying about, it is doubly hard to put materials together to build solid storm defences. It is not impossible, but it is challenging.

From my early years, my saving grace has been the recognition that I need a personal faith in God that is grounded in His mercy and love. My journey with God has been a rollercoaster ride, but my total dependence on God as Father, Confidant, and Best Friend is the best storm defence there is. Time and time again, I have drawn on His comfort and grace through His Word. This has not only kept me standing but has also given me the resilience and resolve to help others in their new normal journey.

#

In my personal circumstances, I have had to ask myself a few questions:

At what point did my journey to a new normal begin?

Do things ever go back to the way they were prior to the trauma?

Depending on the answer to the second question, how will I deal with the fallout of a lasting change that I did not choose?

The new normal journey is never a straightforward process. My personal story is a case in point. My first taste of a new normal was in the immediate aftermath of the prophylactic surgery. Up until that point, my longest stay in hospital had been four days (after the caesarean delivery of Amy). Even though I was no stranger to major surgery, the length of the big surgery itself meant that my eight-day hospital stay took a more significant toll on my body than I had expected.

No amount of research can prepare you for the fact that your body has changed beyond all recognition, not to mention the high pain levels you must endure. In this respect, I would say that my new normal journey began when I woke up after my 12-hour surgery without any concept of time.

In the first six weeks after surgery, I battled a sense of helplessness and frustration at my inability to do things for myself and the necessity of relying on others. Even though I had talked it through with the psychologist before the event, it was not easy. I found it particularly challenging to lean more on Amy; there was a sense of having failed her as a mother. It goes without saying that the feeling was irrational, but the pain of that stayed with me for a long time.

The second phase of my new normal journey was when I got the breast cancer diagnosis. Just when I thought I could start coming up for air, my head was dunked into the deep sea of shock, confusion, and anger. Yes, there was a measure of relief that it was discovered quickly, but there was also the anger that taking the radical step of prophylactic surgery did not spare me from the scourge of this wrecking ball called cancer. Without my faith in God, I would have been a wreck for certain.

Do things ever go back to the way they were prior to the trauma? Probably not. When trauma hits, it blows one's life apart, the ripple effect impacting one's closest and dearest. Picking up the pieces and putting them together will not result in a life resembling the one you had before.

Now that we have got that out of the way, the next issue to address is this: How will I deal with the fallout of a lasting change that I did not choose?

One of trauma's consequences is a shift of perspective. After one's life or that of a loved one is devastated by trauma, one understands that life is way too short to sweat the small stuff. By this, I mean not being overly worried about inconsequential things such as a day job or physical appearance.

Let's consider the importance of a job. In the ordinary course of living, a day job is often the sole means of providing for one's needs and one's household. Trauma, however, is no respecter of job or profession. This means that the ability to carry out daily duties is often one of the first things that gets disrupted. With this disruption comes a need for readjustment. For example, if you are in hospital facing a life-threatening illness or injury, your job will have to take a backseat as you undergo treatment, rehabilitation, and recovery, which can take a considerable length of time.

I remember that one of the things that initially irritated me after my diagnosis was the fact that my time off from my day job had to be extended by a couple of months. However, correct perspective was restored. My health and well-being took precedence over any job – no matter how fantastic it was. In the same way, my concern about physical appearance gave way to expediency and comfort without any quibble on my part.

In the overall scheme of things, I realised that even if I lost my day job or was not impeccably dressed, those things were of no consequence within the context of life-and-death situations.

In most cases of trauma, two difficult issues to contend with are fatigue and pain, both of which can be chronic and debilitating. These issues affect not only the person concerned but also loved ones. Being weak or vulnerable is a position that I used to do my best to avoid. Reeling from the impact of two major surgeries within a nine-week period, as well as the side effects of medication, woke me up to the fact that I had to practice physical and emotional self-care.

Old habits die hard. I would like to say that I embraced my new normal with relative ease, but that is simply not the case. What I did know was that every single decision I made did not just impact my life; Amy was directly affected too. This gave me the impetus to get to grips with my limitations as well as adjust the unrealistic expectations I had of myself.

#

Since you have read this far, I presume that you want to know where my story has brought me. In-between many hospital appointments and more follow-up surgeries (over a three-year period, I ended up having five surgeries in total), there were and sometimes still are some difficult times. Right after my diagnosis, I made up my mind that I would not be defined by this wrecking ball called cancer. I have always been drawn to stories of survival and beating the odds in the face of unimaginable trauma, so I started reading more of these. In times of horrendous pain, they encouraged and inspired me greatly.

As months passed, I realised that I wanted to do more than just survive. I wanted to thrive and live a fulfilling life. People react to trauma in two different ways: they are either buried beneath the rubble of devastation or they rise above it, building something beautiful with the broken pieces they are left with. This section of the book is addressed to the latter group. They are those who, despite the difficulties, know that they were created to fulfil a purpose and benefit humanity. Even though their physical limitations might rule out certain activities, there are still possibilities.

Over the years, I have spoken to and encouraged many people who have gone through various kinds of traumatic events. It is ironic that the last three years since my cancer diagnosis have given me the credibility to offer hope to more people.

There are seven steps that I have used and still use in navigating my new normal. These steps apply to anyone who has been affected by the trauma of serious illness, injury, or bereavement.

The seven steps for navigating your new normal are these:

I.   Realism
II.   Refinement
III. Recognition
IV. Rediscovery
V.   Reconfiguration
VI. Resolution
VII. Realisation

STEP I
Realism

Realism is defined as the attitude or practice of accepting a situation as it is and being prepared to deal with it. In other words, acceptance of reality without the baggage of self-pity.

If you feel that your life has been a catalogue of traumatic events of such magnitude that they could easily crush you, then feeling sorry for yourself will not be hard. After all, you can look around at friends and acquaintances who seem to catch a break from trauma for the better part of their lives.

However, the hard truth is this: self-pity is a close relative of despair and despondency. Carrying the baggage of self-pity can send you down a slippery slope into an abyss of depression that becomes incredibly difficult to get out of. Please note the use of the word *can*. The above statement does not hold true in every case. This is just a word of caution.

The onset of trauma can be so devastating that the mind may deal with it by temporarily blocking out the salient facts and their attendant impact. Those who have gone through trauma often describe events as 'unreal' or 'as if they were happening to someone else'. This may be the case whether they were fully conscious or not. This blocking mechanism means that they are in denial about their situation and believe that this is something that happens only to 'other' people.

Denial is considered one of the most primitive defence mechanisms; it goes back to early childhood development. Denial is the exact opposite of realism in this context.

Denial manifests itself in various forms. An extreme form is wanting to act on the facts of trauma in an autopilot fashion without processing the emotional and psychological impacts. For example, this can be seen when someone is dealing with bereavement. Due to the shock of loss, they latch on to dealing with practicalities as they fear sinking into the abyss of grief. This can manifest itself in engagement in frenzied activities to sort out the funeral, making calls and sending out notifications. While these activities are necessary, there comes a time when realism has to become a priority.

If you are dealing with, caring for, or helping someone who has just gone through a traumatic experience, it may seem that they are 'all okay' because they are coasting along, carrying out activities, and dealing with life as usual. They may simply be in denial. Do not take a cue from their being 'okay' so that you just let them be. Realism may not have set in yet; they need you now more than ever.

You are probably wondering what I mean by all this, after all, you are not a mind reader. You also want to respect the wishes of your loved ones by giving them the dignity they deserve during the turmoil.

My suggestion is to arm yourself with knowledge. Thanks to the internet, we have a wealth of information at our fingertips. As I have previously stated, using my personal experience, get evidence-based information from websites of reputable organisations about what to expect in various situations. Whilst the information you get is not one-size-fits-all, you will find common threads that will help you know what to look out for and how to offer support sensitively. You will also be able to find avenues of support for yourself in the process.

#

Why is realism important?

From the onset of trauma, no matter the cause, life as you know it has changed forever. There is no sugar-coating that fact. To confront and properly address what the impact of the trauma will be in the short and long term, acceptance of the situation on the ground is crucial.

Acceptance enables you to start mapping out a way forward into the future as opposed to being stuck at the point of impact. It gives you permission to embrace the difference between life as it used to be and life as you now know it. In other words, permission to embrace your new normal.

Trauma is like a freight train without brakes running over you. Burying your head in the sand is a non-starter; the train will keep going regardless. In order not to be crushed under the weight of it, you must find a way to get out from underneath. Whether you roll out or crawl painfully, you must make the choice *not* to be crushed.

In choosing not to be crushed under the weight of trauma, one has invariably chosen to rise above it somehow. This is where the issue of resilience comes in. There is no doubt that some people are more resilient than others. In all the definitions of resilience that I have checked out, the common concept is that of *elasticity*. Resilience is the quality of bouncing back no matter how hard one is stretched by adverse circumstances. This often looks like vulnerability mixed with a determination not to sink into the depths of despair. This speaks to an inner strength of character, which is as diverse as individuality.

Given that the ability to bounce back is a character trait, does that mean that those who do not possess great inner strength cannot bounce back from the trauma of serious illness, injury, or bereavement? Not at all. Inner strength is a quality that can and should be bolstered all throughout life. *It is a choice.* If you decide that you want to thrive after trauma as opposed to eking out your survival, you must follow through by making the determination to develop inner strength. It goes without saying that at times this might be difficult, so difficult that it squeezes everything out of you and then some.

#

What does realism look like in practice?

Acceptance is one side of realism; a refusal to settle for less than your capability or worth is another.

Two crucial factors will consistently run through the whole of this new normal journey: *belief systems* and *support networks*. These are important parts of everyday life. However, after the onset of trauma, they are so crucial as to make the difference between rising above it or being crushed under its weight.

Your belief system is the lens through which you view yourself. Your support system is formed by the people you are surrounded by who love you and are prepared to help you, and vice versa.

On a personal level, my sense of worth is rooted in my being made in the image of God, and therefore I know that I am His masterpiece. This one statement was a rallying truth, especially when dealing with body image issues in the aftermath of my surgeries. I am grounded in the knowledge that I am more than just my physical body. I am made in the image of God as a spirit being with a body. Therefore, my self-worth is not tied to my body shape, size, or the smoothness of my flesh. Surgery could alter my body but not my image.

On my journey, I have been blessed with an amazing support network: family, friends, and medical professionals who at various stages have helped me in my realism journey. From the nurses who have encouraged me to see beyond messy wounds to friends who told me the truth in love when I needed to hear it – without them, I would have been a wreck and unable to deal with the reality of my new normal journey.

#

How do I know if I have crossed from denial into realism?

You know you are getting into realism when you have accepted the new normal and begin to take practical steps to map out a way forward into the future as opposed to remaining at the point of impact. To further illustrate what realism looks like in practice, I will use three fictional scenarios that are loosely based on real-life examples that I have seen over the years.

Realism After Serious Illness Diagnosis:

Mandy is a 55-year-old woman who was told five weeks ago that she has terminal bowel cancer and only six months to live. Mandy was given the news along with her husband, James, who has attended all her appointments with her.

After the initial shock, they broke the news to their three adult children. Mandy told her family that she wanted to enjoy her time with them no matter how short or long that might be.

She took the time to digest all the information she was given as well as get information from other reliable sources before she decided on her treatment plan. She also got medical advice on what leisure activities she could take part in to maintain as good a quality of life as she could manage.

Since then, she has gone on a fun weekend trip with her entire family. Even though she slept a lot due to depleted energy levels and other unpleasant side effects from medication, she had a good time with her family creating lovely memories.

In the above example, there is no doubt that the situation is a grim one. After the initial shock, the decision Mandy made about wanting to enjoy whatever time she had left gave her the impetus to move forward despite the painful and uncertain times ahead of her and her family.

She could have chosen to stay in bed and rest in-between hospital appointments. If that were the limit of her capabilities, that would have been fine. However, she knew that with the support of her family, she could make more good memories and that her life had not ended.

Realism After Serious Injury:

Femi is a fit and energetic 24-year-old man who had his left foot amputated from the knee down after being involved in a severe car accident a year ago. Prior to the accident, Femi was a professional athlete who had won medals for his country at international competitions.

In the immediate aftermath of the trauma, he spent three months in hospital. He was angry and felt sorry for himself for weeks. With the support of his medical team and loved ones, he emerged from the fog of depression that nearly consumed him. The turning point was when he accepted that even though he could no longer continue with his previous career, there are so many other things he could still do and make a success of.

He decided to put his athletic training to use to facilitate his rehabilitation. He is now becoming more adept at using his wheelchair, is about to start university, and is also raising funds to get a prosthetic leg that will give him more independence in his daily life.

Anger and shock after trauma are normal reactions. However, if these are allowed to linger too long, they can lead to self-pity and depression. Depending on each person's personality, the depression can be severe or mild. The fact that some people go through depression or any other mental health issue *does not* make them weak. If medication and/or therapy is required, taking that on board is part of dealing with the trauma. Truth be told, until you have been knocked for six, you cannot predict how you will go through it.

This is where having a good support system in place and making the most of it is so important. In Femi's case, his family and friends were the first to notice that he was sinking into depression. They challenged him to confront it by talking to his medical team about it. This was a vital step toward his acceptance of his situation and not settling for less than he knew he was capable of.

Realism after bereavement:

Diego and Sofia's only child, Maria, died 18 months ago after contracting meningitis at the age of 20. She was unconscious within 24 hours of hospital admission and never regained consciousness before her death 48 hours later with her parents by her side.

The bereavement has been a blow to both parents, but Sofia has taken it harder. For the first year, she slept in Maria's room and kept everything the same, as if she were still coming home. Sofia's doctor placed her on antidepressants as she was severely depressed unable to leave her home for weeks on end.

Diego had to look after her and beg well-meaning neighbours to take turns checking up on her.

In that first year, Sofia could not accept that Maria was gone, and she refused all offers of therapeutic support. At the end of the first year, Diego could no longer cope; he was in danger of losing his job and their home. When Diego threatened to leave, that shocked Sofia into accepting the therapeutic support of a psychologist and attending a local bereaved mothers' support group. Sofia has now accepted that her daughter is gone and is beginning to pack up her stuff.

Sofia's inability to accept her daughter's death initially kept her frozen, unable to move on from the initial shock of bereavement. This meant that she was unable to go through the stages of grief that she needed to, and that added pressure on her husband, who was also grieving. In the case of bereavement, there is a finality that makes one conscious of a loved one's absence while making acceptance difficult. If acceptance is proving impossible, one should seek therapeutic support.

Most Christians face the dilemma of recognising reality at the same time as having faith for a change. This is particularly challenging when there has been a previous example of a miraculous change. How does this work? Are these two actions mutually exclusive? Some might argue that accepting reality is tantamount to unbelief. That is *not* the case.

One notable example is of David when he lost his son after praying for him (2 Samuel 12:15–23). His reasoning was that whilst his son was alive, he could pray for a miraculous intervention. However, once his son died, he acknowledged what had happened and moved on as best he could. There have been instances when people have refused to accept the verdict of death and either had a miracle, or the death occurred anyway.

There are no comfortable answers to this dilemma, but my personal take on it lies at the core of what I believe. If I only trust God when things are easy, then I am being selective about which parts of His Word – the Bible – I put my faith in. I cannot claim to be an authentic Christian if I only believe the easy parts and discount the difficult parts.

Jesus did not promise us a hassle-free life. What He promised was victory in spite of great troubles. I have experienced the loss of family members in spite of having faith for a turnaround, and my way of dealing with reality is to do things that I am capable of while holding on to faith.

STEP II

Refinement

'In school, you're taught a lesson and then given a test. In life, you're given a test that teaches you a lesson.'

— *Tom Bodett*

Refinement involves improvement and the removal of unwanted parts. By their very nature, traumatic events teach you valuable lessons. These lessons should, on the whole, make you a better person, provided you are willing to learn them.

A good analogy for these lessons comes from the process of refining gold. One of the oldest methods of gold refinement uses flame at very high temperatures. According to Britannica.com, the melting point of gold is 1,064°C. (In contrast, the melting point of tin is 231.88°C). The gold is placed in a crucible, placed over the heat source, stirred, and skimmed to remove the impurities that rise to the top of the molten metal. The heat must melt the metal for the impurities to be revealed.

With the high levels of heat and the intricate process involved, it is clear that the refinement of gold is not an easy process. This accounts for the fact that gold in its purest form is very expensive. The purity of high-end gold comes at the premium cost of the refining process.

In the same vein, the intensity of trauma tests one's mettle regardless of the cause. Just as fire reveals impurities in gold, nothing shows what you are made of more clearly than trauma. The good, the bad, and the ugly are displayed in technicolour. It is crucial to acknowledge the good that is revealed and celebrate it even as you deal with the negatives. Without this balance, refinement becomes a tool for self-flagellation, which is of no positive benefit at all. Refinement is a lifelong process.

#

The first lessons and improvements you will experience in the aftermath of trauma are the internal ones. When dealing with serious illness, injury, or bereavement, you soon discover what your coping mechanisms are and whether they are suited to your new normal journey.

For example, if you have always had a dismal view of life, how will that serve you in what will certainly be a difficult journey anyway? On the other hand, if you are an eternal optimist with a rose-tinted view of life, how will that help you adjust to the added challenges of the new normal?

With either of these two extreme outlooks, you will do yourself a gross disservice. You must find a middle ground that is best suited to your personal circumstances. As an eternal optimist, you will have to embrace the harshness of the trauma but not allow it to crush your spirit. If you are a pessimist, your outlook will have to undergo a seismic shift; otherwise, you will struggle to believe that there is any hope.

No matter on which side of the divide you find yourself, the big question is this: Are you prepared to learn the lessons you need to learn? Without a doubt, finding the inner strength to become a better person by learning the lessons that trauma teaches can be a hard step. These lessons deal with unseen thought processes that can be masked for extended periods with others none the wiser. Going through the motions and putting on a fake smile are some of the coping mechanisms that people use. However, sooner or later, the mask will slip off, and the smiles will crack or shatter completely.

#

The second set of lessons are the external ones. These are invariably linked to the internal lessons. *People* and *things* come under this category.

Relationships are as complex as people. Whilst some relationships are more predictable than others, no-one can foretell how your nearest and dearest will handle your trauma. If you are the loved one of someone who has been through the wringer, you may have reacted in ways that surprised all who knew you. One thing is certain though: Trauma tests the strength of every relationship. Even relationships that appeared strong before can splinter as cracks that had been ignored for a long time make their presence known.

As your relationships undergo this test, you will learn a lot about your loved ones and your interactions with them. With fragmented family relationships, trauma offers the opportunity to heal or mend bridges where possible. It goes without saying that the other parties must be willing to engage in the process, or it becomes an exercise in futility. Pride is a cold bedfellow, so you will need to bury it if you are going to move forward.

You may have some relationships that are not fruitful or – worse still – toxic and destructive. These are associations that you might have to let go of. With respect to very close family relationships, new rules of engagement might have to be negotiated for the sake of peace and harmony. The rule of thumb is *not* to make a permanent decision based on a temporary situation. No-one can make that kind of decision for you because you have to live with the aftermath and factor in the ripple effect on your loved ones. If this is an area where you require support, do not be too proud to ask for help. I recommend that you seek professional or trusted unbiased counsel to lend you the objectivity to make the best decision for yourself.

Moving on to *things*, this will be very short. Let's face it: Material possessions are just that – things. Yes, you might have paid a lot of money for them, but they are only things. In the aftermath of a traumatic event, you may need to assess your attachment to things, especially if it borders on the obsessive and unhealthy.

What you need to consider is that some of your old possessions may not fit your new normal journey. At some point, you will have to let go of those things to make room for the new things that are suited to your current life experience. For example, if you now need to rely on crutches to get around when previously you could do cartwheels in six-inch heels, you might have to exchange the heels for sports shoes.

#

I will offer a suggestion that might help you articulate the lessons that your trauma is teaching you: journaling. With the array of technology at our disposal, many of us have gotten out of the habit of writing with pen and paper. I, however, believe that there is something very soothing and therapeutic about putting your thoughts down without any care about grammar or any other kind of restriction. Your journal is a keeper of your innermost secrets and a friend that gives you the permission to express yourself in whatever way you choose.

By articulating your thoughts and feelings on a consistent basis, you enable yourself to view the change in your perspective or areas in which you are stuck. There are quite a few books on journaling, but I believe that the best way is just to start.

If you have never journaled before, have fun visiting a bookstore or art supply shop and choosing your materials. As someone who loves pen and paper, I always have a wide variety of pens in different colours. Since I have issues with both my wrists, I tend to use pens that glide on the paper. I also use spiral notebooks, as I find it easier to turn the pages when I am on the go.

The most important thing is *not* to overthink the journaling process. If you are consistent about writing down your thoughts and feelings and what you are learning, it will be a rewarding experience.

Go back and read your previous entries periodically, maybe once a month or every couple of months. You will be amazed at how far you have come since your trauma began. Over the last three years since my major surgery and diagnosis, I have been astounded at how far I have come through the pages of my journals. I also see the areas for improvement. These then shape my goals for the future. If you are unable to journal in the way of writing due to injury or a health issue, there is always another way. Use your smartphone or a similar device to record your thoughts and feelings. At a later date, you can transcribe the audio journal or listen to it as often as you wish.

STEP III
Recognition

'I am God's masterpiece. The pinnacle of His creation. Cancer can try, but it cannot and will not be allowed to take that away from me.'

– Bamidele Adenipekun

The above quote sounds like fighting talk, and I suppose in a way it is. Trauma of any kind will get to your core and threaten to tear apart everything that it can. It is like a marauder, an intruder, getting into places that you thought were solely yours. If your house is invaded by a thief, the instinct of fight/flight/freeze kicks in. Common sense might dictate that you initially freeze, especially if there is a dangerous weapon, involved, but eventually, you must decide what you will guard at all costs. By now, I hope you realise that I am not referring to material things. I am talking about your identity.

Even though cancer was a known enemy, it came uninvited and unexpected into my life. I never thought my identity would be touched, but it was given a good kicking at one point. The fact that I am writing this shows that

I did not just roll over. I came up fighting. I felt that it was important to hold on to who I am as a unique and talented individual, *not* just a cancer patient-cum-survivor.

The process of recognising who you are apart from the trauma that you or your loved one has experienced can be an arduous one. There is no doubt that you have changed in ways that you cannot even begin to articulate. There is no clear demarcation between what life used to be and what it has now become. The question you must ask yourself is this: Who are you now? How do you identify yourself apart from your given name? This might seem too abstract, so I will use myself as a guinea pig.

You already know the basics: I am a 40-year-old woman who was diagnosed with breast cancer at age 37. I was a plastic surgery patient for three years and, on paper, am still a breast cancer patient. If I were to define myself before surgery and diagnosis, I would say that I was a very intelligent, fashionable, fun-loving black Christian woman who enjoyed reading, singing, cooking, and entertaining, just to name a few of my favourite activities. I had also been 100% body-confident for over a decade before my diagnosis.

#

What has changed, and how do I now define/describe myself?

In the aftermath of surgery, the first thing to take a battering was my body image. Here I was, a woman who had counselled and encouraged other women over the years to love their diverse bodies, now struggling not to loathe my own body. I suppose you could say I was vain to think the initial scarring and wounds ugly – guilty as charged. If truth be told, there is an element of vanity in each one of us, whether we acknowledge it or not.

Before surgery, I had spent considerable time reading up and acquainting myself with the changes that my body would undergo. Nevertheless, I was shocked at the transformation. Theory and reality are poles apart, as I quickly discovered. I would like to say that the recovery of my body confidence was a quick one or that I accomplished it all on my own, but that would be untrue.

Once I realised that this was an issue, I cast my mind back to when I had the same struggle in my late teens and early twenties. I started reaffirming myself by replacing negative statements about my body with positive ones. I also decided to believe the positive affirmations of close friends and medical professionals. Three years on, I can finally say that I love my body again. My physical scars are now a celebration of the strong woman that I am.

As a black woman, I used to have so much fun changing my hairstyle once every six weeks to create a different look that fascinated me. Because of cancer medication, my previous hairstyles became uncomfortable. Not to mention that my hair was not as strong as it used to be, a fact I only discovered when my hair fell out two years post-diagnosis. The adjustment to my new hairstyle has been a surprisingly easy one.

One of the things I'd always loved about myself was my intelligence. About six months after my diagnosis, I realised that I had started to become forgetful. I would lose my train of thought and forget what I was about to say mid-sentence. At its worst, my memory issues affected my productivity in the administrative job I had done before without any problems. At home, Amy saw a major difference as well.

Rather than think of myself as becoming dumb, however, I have devised my own way around it. My intelligence is still very much present. The fact that it takes me a little bit longer to get things done is just part of the wonderful person that I now am.

I could go on about how reduced energy levels and long-term pain has curtailed my previous activities. Without a doubt, I have made adjustments, and I still make them as required. The important thing is that I have not allowed any limitation to define me or stop me from being me.

#

Now the question is directed at you, the reader.

Who are you? A trauma survivor or a unique and talented individual? You might say that they are one and the same. I agree with you. The issue is whether you live your life embracing that truth. If, for example, you used to define yourself by your roles or profession, who are you now that those are no longer available to you? If you can no longer do what you used to love because of an injury, who are you now? Beneath the façade you present to the world, are you struggling to discover who you are now on the other side of the trauma that you or your loved one has experienced?

You are probably reading this and wondering if I can begin to comprehend how much time and effort you invested into your previous roles and your huge accomplishments. The truth is that I am not in your shoes. But ask yourself this: What is it worth to you and your loved ones to dig deep and find out who you are outside of your previous roles or passions?

I want you to get hold of your journal and pen for an important exercise. On the blank page in front of you, write the heading 'Who am I?' Make a list of all the things that define you. This is not an exercise to be rushed, so take your time.

If you are like many people, you will probably start with your name. The rest might be more difficult than you anticipate, but the point is for you to dig deep to find who you are behind your functions or roles. If you find this exercise a challenge, enlist the help of someone who knows you well (preferably not directly affected by the trauma). This might lend some helpful objectivity to the much-needed unravelling of your identity.

Your core values and belief system will play an important role in this. Mine are clearly stated in the quote at the start of the chapter, and this has been pivotal in not losing my identity after trauma.

#

Before I end this chapter, I want to address the issue of bereavement and identity. This is a huge topic that deserves a whole book on its own. The finality of death is one that will always rock our worlds as mortals. Even as a Christian who believes in life after death, I still find that the separation on this side of heaven cuts me to the quick. As I stated earlier, my first acquaintance with bereavement was at the age of 17 when I lost my mother. The only way I could find my identity after that loss was to discover whom God had made me to be – a journey that took years.

I will now tread very carefully into an area of loss that I have no experience of whatsoever: the loss of a spouse or child. I am not in any way minimising the impact of other kinds of loss, but because this group has roles attached to it that often form the bedrock of people's identity, it is important to highlight it.

Do you stop being a spouse or parent after the loss of your loved one? The short answer is no. If you are struggling to define who you are, my advice is to cast your mind back to how you saw yourself before your loved one be-came part of your life. For some, it might be a struggle to remember; may have spent most of your life being a parent or spouse. However, there is a man or woman deep within, if you can dig deep enough. To do this, you might require professional support or the help of someone very close. If you do, do not be afraid to look around and ask.

STEP IV

Rediscovery

'To achieve your potential, you'll have to rediscover the joy.'

— *Amanda Borden, Olympic athlete*

According to the Collins Dictionary, 'the rediscovery of something good that you had forgotten or lost is the fact or process of becoming aware of it again or finding it again.'

This step is about claiming back the qualities that make you unique as well as those that are essential for living a fulfilling life. The qualities I will mention are confidence, hope, and joy. Many others could be added to the list, but these are the ones that apply to everyone.

Reading this, you might wonder how it is possible to have forgotten such wonderful qualities that enrich daily living. Each person's experience of trauma is different. For some, the outlook might be so bleak or the impact so far-reaching that there appears to be no silver lining in the dark clouds that have hung around for so long. You might have forgotten or lost your confidence, hope, and joy, so you either need to become aware of them or find them.

The process of rediscovering these three qualities is interconnected with the recognition of who you truly are apart from the ordeal you are going through. Due to the messy nature of trauma, the process of claiming these back is not the same as it might be for those who are just setting goals or improving themselves. For the new normal journey, there is a rebuilding process that must take place.

Confidence

Being assured of oneself and one's abilities is not a quality that comes naturally to everyone. Under normal circumstances, confidence-building exercises are accessible to most people with or without professional support. Within the context of the new normal journey, the landscape is different, so there is another element to rediscovering confidence. The fictional examples introduced earlier will be used to illustrate this point.

Mandy – Prior to her terminal cancer diagnosis, she was a high-flying business executive who had done very well for herself in a financial career spanning over 30 years. By virtue of her position and success, Mandy had been a confident, beautiful woman who was always impeccably dressed.

In the first two months after diagnosis, she has lost her hair, her weight has plummeted, and she spends most of the day in bed totally drained from the effects of her treatment. Due to her poor prognosis, she has had to take medical retirement.

Mandy has now lost her confidence as she is unable to perform her usual tasks in both her professional and family lives. The most basic tasks have become a challenge, and to top it all, she finds cognitive tasks very difficult. Mandy is now a shadow of her former self. With the support of her loved ones, she is having therapeutic support from her local cancer charity by telephone as she is unable to travel.

Some might make the point that, given Mandy's circumstances, rediscovering her confidence is not a priority. I beg to differ.

Confidence has always been part of her makeup, something that her loved ones appreciated and she loved about herself. This is about restoring her dignity. No matter how long or short one's new normal journey is, claiming back the essence of oneself is crucial.

In Mandy's case, after she was diagnosed, her wish was to enjoy life as much as possible with her loved ones. The key to rediscovering her confidence will be to remind her that the real woman is still within even though her physical symptoms might say otherwise. This may take the form of completing simple tasks like listening to audiobooks (as she has always been an avid reader) or going shopping with her best friend for a stylish wig. Whilst these activities might appear small to someone else, in Mandy's situation the boost of confidence would help her to live a life that is meaningful to her.

Joy

Joy is often used interchangeably with happiness, but I believe they are very different emotions. I am not going by the dictionary definition of the two. Here is my definition: Happiness is dependent on something positive happening, giving cause to celebrate, whereas joy is a state of the soul that remains even when circumstances are unpleasant.

'In the world, you will have tribulation but be of good cheer, I have overcome the world.'

— John 16:33

'Consider it pure joy, my brothers and sisters, whenever you face trials of many kinds.'

— James 1:2 (NIV)

The two verses above are from the Bible. The first one is a quote by Jesus. He knew what great trouble meant, not just in the way He was reviled during His earthly ministry but also in His death on the cross. The second verse, written by one of Jesus's disciples, appears to make light of difficult times.

Both Jesus and James had first-hand experiences of traumatic events in their lives. Speaking about joy, therefore, means that their emotions were not dictated by their circumstances, which were often grim. As a Christian, I define joy as a deep-seated peace and assurance that I am a child of God, and He is watching over me no matter what I go through.

Despite knowing this, I have had to rediscover my joy at various points in this new normal journey. Trauma of any kind can keep you bound by negative feelings like bitterness, resentment, self-pity, etc. It can be hard not to get bogged down by the weight of all these, especially if things do not appear to improve as quickly as you want. Living with pain on a consistent basis for years can be such a draining process that joy might seem to have gone on a long break.

I keep rediscovering my joy again and again by staying rooted in my faith in God. This has helped me keep my sanity through intense struggles. I fundamentally believe that God is good; His Word says so, and I take Him at

His word wholeheartedly. That is the foundation of my faith.

How you rediscover your joy will depend on what you believe at your core. Trauma is a testing ground for your belief system. Nowhere is this more apparent than in the rediscovery of joy. Resilience does not exist in a vacuum – joy is one of the things that builds resilience. That is why you so often see or hear of people who can inspire others even when they have suffered unspeakable tragedies themselves.

Hope

Hope is the feeling that you will have what you want, that the outcome of events will be what you expect or something else good. Despair, the opposite, is the loss of hope. Despair can become the starting point for depression.

Traumatic events, by their very nature, are the antithesis of hope. They throw into our lives what we neither want nor expect. In the new normal journey, it is important to rediscover hope. Otherwise, you will not have the required impetus to proceed into a life of fulfilment.

In psychology, hope is recognised as a vehicle for the achievement of goals. C. R. Snyder, along with his colleagues, came up with the hope theory:

> 'The advantages of elevated hope are many. Higher as compared with lower hope people have a greater number of goals, have more difficult goals, have success at achieving their goals, perceive their goals as challenges, have greater happiness and less distress, have superior coping skills, recover better from physical injury and report less burnout at work, to name but a few advantages.'

To choose hope when circumstances might dictate otherwise takes an act of will that has to come from within the individual. You must will yourself to live beyond mere existence.

STEP V
Reconfiguration

'The pessimist complains about the wind; the optimist expects it to change; the realist adjusts the sails.'
— *William Arthur Ward*

As anyone who has been affected by trauma will tell you, it comes with the force of a wrecking ball smashing at your life and the lives of your loved ones. It is a given that trauma will change the shape of one's life to a large or small degree. The way you envisioned the map of your life will undergo a shift not of your own choosing. A relatively straightforward life map can be blown to smithereens in an instant. All you can do is pick up the pieces that remain to create another map that has no resemblance to anything you have ever seen before.

If you have ever gone on a journey and encountered a series of diversions (perhaps due to an accident), you can appreciate the inconvenience of finding alternative routes. That, of course, is something that you get over as soon as you reach the end of your trip. Unfortunately, trauma does not come with a set of directions showing the destination.

You must make choices about what your reconfigured life map will look like in the new normal. Illness, injury, or bereavement often bring immediate practicalities that will force you to make certain decisions sooner than you envisage. This can include short-term decisions that involve loved ones and livelihoods. Whilst some of these decisions might be cushioned by financial means, there are some that will hurt regardless of socioeconomic status.

In making the life-changing decisions that this step requires, it is important to assess your top priorities so that you do not lose sight of what is important in the chaos. For example, if providing for your loved ones is your biggest priority, trying to ensure that their standard of living is not affected might drive you to focus excessively on income-generating ventures at the detriment of spending quality time with them. One of the biggest lessons you learn from surviving trauma is that life is too short not to treasure and nurture to the fullest the loving relationships in your life.

The reconfiguration of your life map will vary widely depending on your circumstances. The choices that are open to a single individual with no dependents will be different to the choices open to someone with a spouse and dependants. No man is an island, so there will always be others who may be affected by the choices you make. It is therefore important, where applicable, to speak to them once you have made your decisions.

As much as possible, avoid making permanent decisions when the condition under consideration is a temporary one. Even though I have mentioned this point before, it bears repeating. Heightened emotions in the aftermath of trauma can often skew your judgement. For example, returning to work sooner than advised by your doctor might hamper your emotional and psychological recovery in the long term.

As much as you care for your loved ones, the decision about what your life map will look like should ultimately be made to suit you. Despite their love for you, your nearest and dearest are often the most resistant to change in the status quo, especially if it comes at an inconvenience to them. This can strain familial relations, especially when you have previously acquiesced to their demands. The disapproval from loved ones can be very painful to deal with, but so is resentment over unrealised dreams. You must decide which route you are prepared to live with.

Your loved ones will know which buttons to press in a bid to get you to comply with their wishes. You may easily fall for emotional blackmail, which can be used to good effect in these circumstances. Do not castigate yourself. Once you realise that you are being manipulated, take action to free yourself and progress in a positive direction.

Old habits die hard. You might require someone who is not emotionally involved to serve as a sounding board and companion on this journey. This does not have to be a professional. It can be a friend whom you respect and who values you and respects your wishes. This must be a positive person who is willing to be truthful without putting you down.

I will use an example to illustrate this point.

Marge is a 72-year-old widow who lost her husband of 50 years nine months ago. A series of strokes left her husband disabled for the last eight years of his life, and Marge was his full-time caregiver. Before caring for her husband, she was a vibrant and outgoing woman who could pass for 20 years younger.

Marge and her husband have two daughters and a son with seven grandchildren between them. They all live within one hour's drive of each other. The family home is a big five-bedroom house that requires a lot of work on Marge's part to keep in impeccable condition.

Her children and grandchildren are busy with their own lives, and Marge is keen to reclaim her life. She wants to sell the family home and buy herself a small two-bedroom apartment in a retirement living community two hours away. She also wants to reconnect with her old friends and start travelling around the world.

Her son supports her decision, as he believes his mother is long overdue for a break. On the other hand, the two daughters – who rely on Marge for their childcare needs – are up in arms. They accuse her of being quick to forget their father and ripping out the heart of the family which, in their opinion, is that home (even though both daughters are in their 40s and haven't lived at home for more than 20 years). They have shown their disapproval of their mother by giving her the cold shoulder since the matter was proposed.

Most people reading this will inwardly berate the selfish daughters for their insensitivity and want to tell Marge to toughen up and move on with her life. It is easy to tell others to grow up or move on. However, in small or big ways, many of us are guilty of the same things. Some people are afraid of the reactions of their loved ones to change the landscape of their new normal. On the other hand, there are some people who they themselves are so stuck in the past that they find any suggestion of change most unwelcome.

What none of Marge's children realised is that her GP had advised her to move. She is depressed because she is surrounded by memories of her late husband, but is unable to make changes for fear of her daughters' reactions.

Marge's best friend Lisa, who lives in the retirement community, has been coming over to visit her more often since the bereavement. When Lisa found out how the daughters reacted, she enlisted the help of Marge's son to arrange for an estate agent to put the house on the market. As the house belongs solely to Marge, there is nothing her daughters can do about her decision to sell.

The cold, hard reality is that the death of Marge's husband has irreversibly changed her life. She knows what she wants her reconfigured life map to look like. Embracing the route change is essential for Marge's emotional and psychological well-being, which must be a priority in her new normal.

STEP VI

Resolution

'There is nothing noble in being superior to your fellow man. True nobility is being superior to your former self.'

– Ernest Hemingway

Resolutions are popularly associated with the start of the year, a time when people are keen to make goals. Most of those who set New Year resolutions do not fulfil them because they have unrealistic expectations. By the end of the first week of January, more than half of these goals have been ditched.

Trauma does not operate on a timetable, so there will never be a convenient time to make goals. You might as well start today. In the short-term, many of your goals might be tied to survival as a matter of necessity. For example, the immediate priority after a major accident might be to breathe unaided and start drinking fluids with a straw as opposed to intravenously. Do not discount the importance of such crucial steps. In the medium to long term though, goals should be tied to the new shape of life as you now know it.

Your reconfigured life map sets the destination; setting goals outlines how you will get there. Even though the word resolution has been given a bad name due to the New Year's fad, there is nothing trivial about its use in this context. To have come this far after a serious illness, injury, or bereavement will have taken a doggedness and fortitude that you might have been surprised you possess.

There are many goal-setting techniques available, but some might not be suited to the kind of goals you have. Using the new life map as a guide, you must ask yourself what you want to see within specific time spans given your circumstances. Some of the goals can be tangible things, and others are intangible. For example, you might be able to set a goal to restart your business in the next six months, once your treatment has ended. On the other hand, you might also decide that you want to carve out more time for leisure activities with loved ones. Only you can determine what more time with loved ones looks like.

#

One of the goal-setting techniques that can be adapted to most new normal situations is the GROW model formulated by Graham Alexander and John Whitmore.

The GROW acronym stands for goals, reality, options, and will.

Goals – Set out what you want to achieve.

It is important that these goals are not an exact replica of the ones you set before the trauma, especially if your present limitations are permanent. However, this does not mean that you cannot set goals that will stretch and challenge you.

For example, within a couple of months after diagnosis, I knew that I wanted to leave my day job and start my dream job. I set myself a timetable of 18 months.

Reality – Explore what your current situation looks like in relation to your stated goals.

Continuing with my personal example – 12 months after setting my goal, it became apparent that there was no way I could give up my day job. I had undergone my third surgery and was preparing myself for the prospect of more. Therefore, I had to extend the timetable, making it flexible enough to accommodate variables like surgery dates and recovery periods.

Options – Outline the steps that you are prepared to take to achieve your goals.

Even though I was initially frustrated by the longer timetable, I realised this was an opportunity to learn the necessary skills to prepare for the new career that I wanted.

Will – Draw up a statement of intent and an action plan.

This is when your resolve and commitment to your goals are tested. As part of my preparation, I embarked upon a year-long course of study to acquire the necessary knowledge for my goal. Taking this course when I was 100% fit would have been enough of a challenge. Pushing through from start to finish with hospital appointments, work, pain, and a minor surgery thrown into the mix pushed my resolve nearly to the breaking point. What kept me going was the support of loved ones as well as the reward of acquiring the tools that would get me to my destination. Writing this book and reaching this point in the ongoing physical and psychological recovery after my fifth and final surgery comes under this step.

#

I am putting a word of caution here. Please note that the steps that I have taken are in no way meant to be a pattern or rule of thumb for your new normal journey. Everyone's experience of trauma is different depending on so many variables: the type of trauma, personality, support systems, and socioeconomic/environmental factors. In choosing to focus on some goals, I made the choice to put others on the backburner until I had the physical and mental stamina to tackle them. I have used my circumstances to illustrate the various stages of the GROW model so that you can adapt it for your personal use.

You may still be reeling from the aftershocks of trauma, unable to see the way ahead. You might not even see the point of making any goals – all your hopes and dreams have been shattered. Take your time to deal with and process what has happened. Activities might fill up the time, but they will not help sort out the jumble of thoughts and feelings running riot in your head.

If you are reading this right now, you are alive. You owe it to yourself to rise from your situation, no matter what that looks like to you. Whatever support you require along the way, do not be afraid or too proud to ask.

I will end this chapter with a quote that makes me smile and puts a spring in my step. I hope it encourages you too.

'The future belongs to those who believe in the beauty of their dreams.'

– Eleanor Roosevelt

STEP VII

Realisation

'Believe in yourself and all that you are. Know that there is something inside you that is greater than any obstacle.'

— *Christian D. Larson*

I hope that this book has challenged you to ask some questions about your new normal journey. Are you charting your course with unbridled hope, or are you being dragged through life barely surviving what you have gone through? Are you a spectator of life, barely aware of the passing hours and days? Trauma is a wrecking ball and a thief. How much more are you willing for it to take from you?

It is time to get in the driver's seat of your life.

What will success look like for you? There has to be a way for you to measure your progress. Every single day that you have breath is an opportunity to take a small step toward your destination. The fact that this goal may be completely different to what you once imagined is *not* a reason to wallow in despair. Savour the joy you have in your life and look forward to tomorrow.

Previously, success might have been determined by your career. Today, you sitting up by the window admiring a picturesque landscape with your loved ones around you might be a good achievement. It is so important to be flexible on the new normal journey. This would make it easier to adapt to the changes and see your new progress for what it truly is. It will also serve as a catalyst for change if you are not moving in the direction that you want.

Your trusted confidant – your journal – will help you with this part. By revisiting your earlier entries (maybe in the first few days after the onset of the trauma) and comparing them with your most recent ones, you will be amazed at how far you have come.

The motivation for achieving your goals is the reward that awaits you when you get there. What are you rewarding yourself with now? Please do not forget to reward yourself when you realise that you have accomplished a goal.

23 years ago, when I lost my mother to cancer, the sense of being cast adrift in the dark tunnel of grief was excruciating, and I never thought I would be whole again. The subsequent havoc that cancer wrought in my sister's life, as well as mine, has been a relentless wave that barely lets me take a breath.

As difficult as the journey has been, my faith in God has grounded and kept me not only standing but also thriving as I make my way towards the ultimate fulfilment of my dreams.

If you are reading this, you are holding in your hands the realisation of my decade-long dream to become an author. You are now part of my new normal. My hope is that I have given you the beginnings of a map for your own new normal journey.

God bless you.

Postscript

26 days after this manuscript was finished, my big sister passed away at the age of 46 after a 5-year battle with metastatic breast cancer. Even though this is not my first experience of loss, it has been doubly devastating as it brings back so many memories of our mother's death 23 years before at the same age.

I was certain that my sister, having valiantly rallied after each setback, would beat this horrid disease.

Now what? The irony has not escaped me that the framework I have developed for others is the very same one that I will now reapply to myself. As you well know, this is not a walk in the park. It is messy and hard. That is just it in a nutshell. However, out of the mess, something beautiful can emerge if I stay true to the process.

I will now give an overview of how I am applying and will keep applying the seven-step new normal process to my own bereavement journey. Take note of the tenses I have used; I understand that this is a long journey, and I cannot predict how long it will take. Some parts will be quicker than others. No matter how my steps falter or how slow they might be, the important thing is to keep moving forward.

Realism

Accepting that one of my closest confidants and supporters is no longer around to cheer me on along life's journey is extremely painful. When I looked at her body in repose, it seemed as if she were sleeping, yet I knew she was gone because there was no movement, no opening of the eye, no smile or wink to show that my loving sister was still with us. Gone, never to be seen again on this side of heaven.

The shock, the numbness, of those early days gave way to a sense of everything being unreal. I imagined that soon I would wake up from the bad dream. In a way, I think dealing with the practicalities in the days following – planning the funeral, informing official bodies, etc. – helped me accept that this was the start of another new normal for me. This new normal meant that I could no longer pick up the phone to share my joy, sorrow, frustration, or excitement with my big sister.

As I previously mentioned in the chapter on realism, support networks and belief systems are crucial at the start of this journey. I am immensely blessed with people around me who share my faith and love me unconditionally. These people give me space to rant and get things off my chest, and they act as truth-tellers when I need them to. The professional support of my local cancer support centre has also been instrumental in helping me not sink into the pit of despair.

As the second sibling in my family, the mantle of being the oldest is one that I now wear with equanimity. This is life as we know it from now on. I choose to see the grace that equips me to do the best I can for my family, and I will not allow the weight of responsibility to crush me. As with every stage in life, sometimes I will do great, and sometimes I will fall flat on my face. I have the deep-seated assurance that there is always enough grace for each day, so I do not have to be crippled by the fear of tomorrow.

Refinement

Grief – with all its attendant cognitive, physiological, emotional, and psychological reactions – has been so intense for me that at times I feel as if I am in the middle of a fire. This refining process is showing me what I am capable of in the positive and negative sense.

For starters, I have come to realise that I do not give myself enough credit for how much I have invested in my own emotional well-being. I have revisited old books that I used for an introductory counselling course and reacquainted myself with the things to watch out for, ensuring that I ask for help when I need it and not just when I get totally overwhelmed.

On the negative side of things, I have learnt that I can be more selfish and less self-controlled than I thought I was. Impatience and intolerance for the weaknesses of others are two of my major issues that this bereavement has highlighted. I see this as an opportunity to work on becoming a better version of myself.

This step is the one I find the hardest, as it forces me to come up with new ways of handling things as opposed to taking the easy way out. That said, this refining process does not mean I will undergo a personality transplant – not by any means! All I know is that, because of my willingness to be more self-aware, I can look back on this time as one of personal growth.

Recognition

I count myself fortunate in having my identity rooted in who I was created to be: a masterpiece, the pinnacle of God's creation. This has been a grounding force in my life. With the loss of my sister, I have had to revisit the issue of my identity again – not so much regarding who I am but regarding my capabilities when a major source of support is gone.

Whilst I will forever mourn the loss of my sister (I would not be human if I did not), I also recognise that I will always carry within me all the attributes that I was born with. This means that, after the initial doubts that came with the 'now what' question, I still have the fire burning within me to make a positive impact on the lives of others.

Yes, there will always be a massive void in my life that my sister filled, but I will excel and do well in spite of it. The sadness and feeling of being robbed of time together will eventually give way to the understanding that the time we did share was a gift that I can treasure always.

Rediscovery

Out of all the steps, this is the one that I think will stretch for a considerable length of time. I am grateful that my joy and confidence are not bound to circumstances; they are rooted in my faith, which remains unshaken. The hard thing, though, is that I have no way of knowing how long it will take before my happiness and sunny disposition are restored in full.

It is still early days. I wish that my sister was here to share good times with, and I have a sense of being partly removed from others' celebrations. I believe that is normal. I have lost two family members at a young age, so it is natural to feel robbed of significant milestones and memories that cannot include them. My consolation is that, with time, my family will create new memories that will be no less significant because we cherish our loved ones' legacies.

In the meantime – taking the rough with the smooth – I accept that, for now, tears and laughter will vie for equal space in my heart. That does not mean that I have lost the essence of who I am; it just means that I am being patient with myself until I get back to a place where I can experience more smiles that tears.

Reconfiguration

Whether I like it or not, a life change has occurred, and there is no going back. In my circumstances, there are responsibilities that I did not have to take on board before that have now become a living reality. The biggest change is in my role as an aunt to my two nieces. Being an aunt when their mum was alive is totally different to being an aunt now that she is gone. One of the things I hope to do well is to keep the memory of their mum alive.

This is new terrain for me, with no manuals or tutorials. All I can do is give it my best shot. As with any new journey, I will take a couple of wrong turns or go the long way to begin with. However, in time the new map will become clearer, and I will find a route that suits me.

So many people who are not walking in your shoes have definite ideas about which path you should take because they 'have more life experience than you'. I have come to realise that what we deem 'life experience' is subjective. There might be people who have lost loved ones to serious illness who have a quicker time of adjustment to their new normal and their might be those whose experience is quite the opposite. I own my journey and will navigate it my way.

Resolution

With this loss has come a renewed and more urgent sense of purpose for me. What has been impressed upon my mind more than anything else is the fragility of life. This is not a new concept for me; I have lost a few dear friends over the years. My sister's death, however, has made me revisit the issue of legacy. When I lost my mother at the age of 17, I remember being impressed by the wonderful legacy she left behind and wondering if it would ever be possible for me to do the same.

As a mature adult, I have come to realise that leaving a lasting positive legacy is a product of intentional living. I cannot dictate how many years I get to live on this planet. Therefore, I want to make each day count for good by impacting lives and making a difference.

Even in the throes of deep grief, this view helps me not to lose sight of my goals. Yes, in this season my progress is not as quick as I would wish, but the important thing is not to be stagnant. That firm resolve is what has got me through writing this extra part of the book less than three months after my sister's death whilst still seeking the support I need to grieve properly.

Realisation

My measure of success is getting this book into the hands of readers who need support in their new normal journey.

Since you are reading this book through to its final – unplanned – section, I know that I have realised one of my goals that my late sister believed in and faithfully supported. Even though she is not here to see the book in its published form, she lived long enough to know that her faith in me was not wasted.

I find that very comforting.

APPENDIX 1
A Hospital Diary

I did not set out to write a hospital diary. If anything, I imagined that all my thoughts surrounding this stint in hospital would remain locked up in my head. However, six days after surgery, I woke up with the title *Bamidele: A Hospital Diary* in my head. I then realised that this was a wonderful opportunity to recount an experience unlike any I had ever had before. An experience never to be forgotten.

Before I delve into the diary itself, I feel it is necessary to reflect on some of my thoughts in the days leading up to the surgery. From the moment my GP suggested the risk-reducing bilateral mastectomy following my sister's diagnosis, I knew that I could no longer downplay the implications of my family history of breast cancer. I have had to come to the realisation that my own awareness of breast health was insufficient to lower my risk of having breast cancer.

From the theoretical knowledge of research to the practical application in my personal case, the last eight months have been a steep learning curve. I have learnt that I will be unable to do much for the first six weeks after this surgery and that I will just have to learn to accept support graciously while my body heals. Even though I have found the preparation time challenging, my understanding of the all-sufficient grace and peace of God has deepened, enriching my life in the process.

27 January 2014 – Surgery Day

The sense of peace and calm that surrounds me is nothing short of amazing. Over the past 10 days or so, that has remained the case. Father, I cannot begin to tell You how grateful I am for Your love and peace which passes all understanding. It is beyond my comprehension, and that is part of the mysterious way in which You move.

Just over an hour before being taken down into the operation theatre, I was listening to worship music and reflecting on the fact that I am His beloved child. Therefore, nothing I am going through or will ever go through will escape His notice or come to Him as a surprise. I am ready to proceed to the next phase of this journey without any sense of disquiet or any doubt whatsoever.

Father, all I can do is worship You in the beauty of holiness.

2 February 2014

What an interesting and varied-nature journey the last six days have been.

When I came around six days ago, it took me quite a while to realise how faithful and merciful the Father has been to me. One moment I was having light conversation and banter with the anaesthetists, the next I was back on the hospital bed, totally out of it due to the number of drugs in my system.

And so, the next phase begins. Having to rely on others for the most basic of bodily functions could easily have been a downer for someone who is as independent as I am. Given the fact that I find it difficult to ask for help under normal circumstances, dependence on the kindness of strangers was a big thing for me.

However, when it came down to it, I was amazed at the grace that I was given to keep my sense of humour and mischief through it all. Yes, my body as a woman will never be the same again. However, the equanimity with which I have been enabled to embrace every single step is nothing short of amazing.

So, what are the facts? After a 12-and-a-half-hour surgery of bilateral mastectomy with immediate reconstruction, I woke up feeling like my belly was put in a vice. I felt slicing pain at intervals despite the medication that I had been given for pain relief. Being an introspective person, I thought that by now I would be a wreck emotionally. Instead, I find that in some ways I feel better psychologically than, say, a couple of months ago. Now, there's no doubt that part of that is relief that this major procedure is over and done with. In the face of physical frailty, I know the reality of being held in the Everlasting Arms.

Over the past few days, every step has been painful and difficult as I learn to do all over again what used to come naturally, like standing upright and walking. What I cannot take for granted is the favour of God that has surrounded me since I have been here.

During the days when I could not have outside visitors because I was not even up to it, all the medical staff that I have met over the last few days came to see me at different intervals so that there was not any time to brood or feel alone. I am not referring to the medical personnel responsible for my care so that it can be argued that they were doing their jobs; I am referring to people who only saw me in passing and came to say hello just because. At one point, a fellow patient commented on how popular I was in the hospital, marvelling at the number of people who were happy just to come and see me.

I took my first steps unaided yesterday. Friends who saw me commented on how well I looked, despite my being in physical pain and discomfort as well as totally exhausted.

Another facet of this journey is how mature and okay Amy has been through it all. When she first came to see me two days after surgery, she looked so smart in her school uniform. She took everything in her stride, not upset about how unwell I looked but just happy to see me, asking if she could help me in any way. I am so grateful for the support of her school staff, especially the head-teacher who brought her to see me and willingly gave her the love and affection that I could not express as I wanted to. Wherever and whenever I have needed help, the Father has provided and exceeded my expectations.

I would like to use this opportunity to encourage any-one who is going through any kind of personal trial, be it for a short or long season. No matter how dark the night, no matter how fierce the storms, do not ever lose your hope in the One who has loved and redeemed you. If you can see and hear Him through the dark and the noise, you know you will never walk alone.

Underneath you are the Eternal Arms. Do not resist; allow yourself to be carried through. It does not matter how old you are or how long you have been a Christian; at one point or another in life's journey, you will need to be carried through like a child in your Father's arms. Not because you are weak or flawed but just as a neces-sary phase in life. The fact that I am writing this from a hospital bed shows that I am by no means making light of the trials you are facing or have faced. I am, however, being taught anew the wonderful heart of the Father – so loving and tender in and out of season.

I have no doubt that in the coming weeks there will be physical and emotional challenges for me to overcome. I do know that through it all He will remain ever-faithful; He will be to me what I need Him to be as the journey unfolds.

In the teary times, He will wipe away every single tear and be my Eternal Comfort.

In physically challenging times, He will come alongside me to be my Tower of Strength.

In times when I feel insecure, I will run into His arms, finding security that the world cannot comprehend.

In sad times, He will give me unalloyed joy.

In the midst of turbulence, He will envelop me with His peace which passes understanding.

In dark times, he will shine the light of His revelation.

Blessed be the Lord our God who daily loads us with benefits. To Him be glory, honour, and adoration now and forevermore.

APPENDIX 2

Questions/Points for Reflection

1. When did your new normal begin? At what point did you realise that life as you know it will never be the same again?

2. How did you feel at that point? Did you acknowledge and deal with your feelings? In part or in full?

3. Did you seek any form of therapeutic support either from professionals or loved ones?

4. If your answer to Questions 2 and 3 is *no*, ask yourself why.

Once questions 1 to 4 have been addressed to some degree, you will be ready to proceed to the next part.

5. What are the changes that you have to make because of the trauma you or your loved one has gone through?

6. Are you currently satisfied with life in your new normal? If you are, do you have a plan in place to keep it that way? If you are not, what are you prepared to do to make a positive change?

7. Do you think you will benefit from coaching to help you achieve the goals you have set for your new normal?

Connect with me at www.inspiredtosoar.co.uk where you will find inspiring blog posts to encourage you on your new normal journey. You will also see coaching programmes designed to support you in the achievement of your goals.

Glossary
Of Medical Terms

Atypical hyperplasia: precancerous condition that affects cells in the breast

Bilateral mastectomy: surgical removal of both breasts, usually as a result of cancer

Biopsy: removal and examination of microscopic tissue in order to determine whether tumour is malignant or benign

Breast reconstruction: series of surgical procedures to recreate a breast

BRCA-1 and BRCA-2: the best-known genes linked to breast cancer risk

ER+: oestrogen-receptor-positive breast cancer cells that may receive signals from oestrogen that could promote their growth

Fibroadenoma: a benign tumour originating from glandular tissue

Gamma Knife: a type of radiation therapy used to treat tumours and other abnormalities in the brain

Histopathology: the study of changes in tissues caused by disease

Invasive DCIS: invasive ductal carcinoma in situ – cluster of malignant cells in breast ducts that has broken through to nearby breast tissue

Laser Ablation: low-level laser therapy used to treat cancer that has spread to the lungs from other areas

Lymph node: each of a number of small swellings in the lymphatic system where lymph is filtered and lymphocytes (types of white blood cells) are formed

Lymphoedema: swelling as a result of obstruction of lymphatic vessels or lymph nodes

Metastasis: the development of secondary malignant growths at a distance from a primary site of cancer

(Definitions obtained from www.online-medical-dictionary.org and www.medical-dictionary.thefreedictionary.com)

Works Cited

Hoffmann, James Edward. "Gold Processing." *Encyclopæ-dia Britannica*. Encyclopædia Britannica, Inc., 11 May 2001. Web. 26 July 2017.

Gold Traders: Gold-Traders (UK) Ltd. "How to Refine Gold." Gold-Traders (UK) Ltd. Gold-Traders (UK) Ltd, 2010. Web. 26 July 2017.

Snyder, C. R. "Conceptualizing, Measuring, and Nurturing Hope." *Journal of Counseling & Development* 73.3 (1995): 355-60. Web.

Whitmore, John. "Grow Model | Sir John Whitmore's Grow Coaching Model Framework." *Performance Consultants*. Performance Consultants International, 2015. Web. 14 July 2017.

Acknowledgements

- My **Father** and my **God** without You sending Your **Son** to save me and Your **Holy Spirit** Counselor guiding me into all truth this would not be at all possible. My life, worship and adoration are 100% yours.

- **Amy** - I am so thankful that you are my daughter. More than any other human being; you have supported and cared for me in this new normal with maturity beyond your years. I love you from the bottom of my heart.

- To my **siblings** – thank you all for supporting, cheering me on and believing in me. I am blessed to do the journey of life with you. I love you all.

- To my church family – **Pastor Michael Williams, Jill Williams** and every member of **Elim Church Swansea** – your prayers and support has been unwavering over the past few years. I am so grateful, more than words can express.

- To **Kary Oberbrunner** – my superb coach with a servant heart, your unwavering belief in me has brought this book from my imagination to life. I am truly grateful for your wise counsel and continuous support.

- To the **Igniting Souls Tribe**: an amazing community of rock stars who have prayed, supported and cheered me on even in the midst of searing loss so that I did not give up when I was tempted to. I am incredibly thankful for each one of you.

- **Mrs Ferriman** and the entire **staff** at **Oakleigh House School** – You all went over and beyond the call of duty to support Amy and me. I am especially grateful for the way you held Amy up when the wrecking ball hit our lives.

- To those who have my unending gratitude for always being there no matter the season. You are used to save my sanity on this roller coaster journey – **Rev Lara Akinola, Sue Williams, Jaunty and Opeyemi Aidamenbor, Lynne Jones, Ade Adewumi, Mary Ojulari, Olayinka Akinyemi, Joanna Andree, Bisola Odukunle, Yinka Lewis, Obi Anyadike, Lloyd and Uche Williams, Ben and Tobi Ugbene, The Akinades, The Iwobis, The Ifies, The Sholiyis.**

- To all the professionals who have looked after me and continue to do so incredibly well mega thanks. Special thanks go to:

- **Mr Amar Ghattaura** my plastic surgeon and his entire team at Morriston Hospital.

- **Ms Dillon** – my breast surgeon and **Ms Alison Marks** – the best breast care nurse I could have asked for

- All the staff and volunteers at **Maggie's Cancer Caring Centre**, Swansea

- All the staff at the **Macmillan Enhanced Cancer Recovery Team, Singleton Hospital** your 100% commitment to my wellbeing on this new normal journey is priceless

- To so many others too numerous to mention who have shown me kindness and empathy on this journey – even though I have not mentioned you by name, I am immensely grateful for your positive input in my life.

About the Author

Bamidele Adenipekun believes that dreams are like birds that require wings to fly. Often, adverse circumstances in life damage the wings of people's dreams. Bamidele's purpose and passion is tending the broken wings of people's dreams so that they can be inspired to soar. She has been writing inspirational posts for over a decade and has a growing following on her Facebook page, where she has also used regular video blogs to inspire others to overcome obstacles that get in the way of their dreams.

An author, coach, and speaker, she is the founder of Inspired To Soar Ltd, which serves people seeking fulfilment in their lives after the devastation caused by the trauma of serious illness, injury, or bereavement. She holds a Master's degree in International Development and Human Rights as well as a Certificate in Life Coaching Studies. No stranger to adversity herself, she is a breast cancer and child abuse survivor and is well acquainted with the pain of bereavement. A former civil servant, her last role was as a bereavement adviser for five years.

She is the single mother of a fabulous daughter and they reside in Wales.

Connect at **www.inspiredtosoar.co.uk**

Lightning Source UK Ltd.
Milton Keynes UK
UKOW06f1809170917
309288UK00011B/213/P